COLDPLAY
THE SINGLES & B-SIDES

CW00740879

Published by
WISE PUBLICATIONS
14-15 Berners Street, London, W1T 3LJ, UK.

Exclusive distributors:
MUSIC SALES LIMITED
Distribution Centre, Newmarket Road,
Bury St Edmunds, Suffolk, IP33 3YB, UK.
MUSIC SALES PTY LIMITED
120 Rothschild Avenue, Rosebery, NSW 2018, Australia.

Order No. AM990550
ISBN 13: 978-1-84772-080-1

This book © Copyright 2007 Wise Publications,
a division of Music Sales Limited.

Edited by Tom Farncombe.
Music arranged by Matt Cowe, Arthur Dick and Martin Shellard.

Printed in the EU.

www.musicsales.com

WISE PUBLICATIONS
part of The Music Sales Group

London / New York / Paris / Sydney / Copenhagen / Berlin / Madrid / Tokyo

1.36

Words & Music by
Guy Berryman, Chris Martin, Jon Buckland & Will Champion

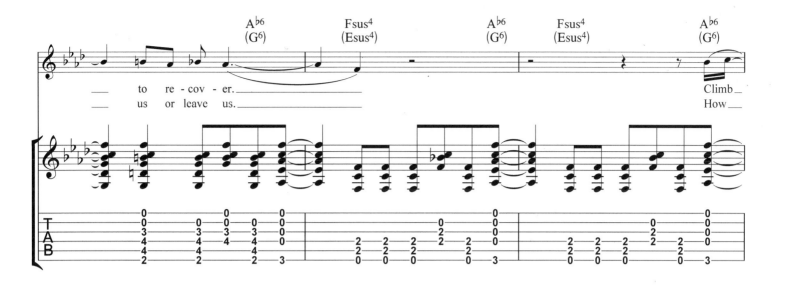

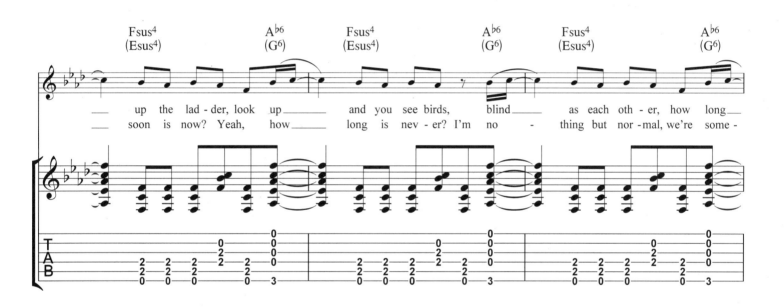

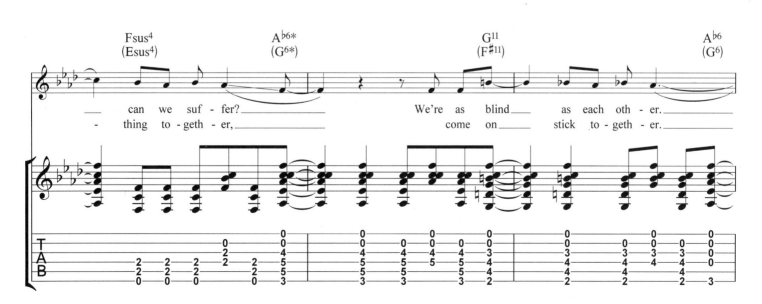

ANIMALS

Words & Music by
Guy Berryman, Jon Buckland, Will Champion & Chris Martin

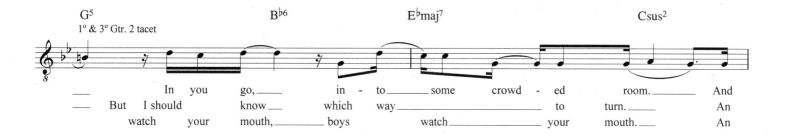

G5   B♭6   E♭maj7   Csus2

1° & 3° Gtr. 2 tacet

___ In you go, _____ in - to _____ some crowd - ed room._____ And
___ But I should know___ which way _____ to turn.___ An
watch your mouth,_____ boys watch_____ your mouth.___ An

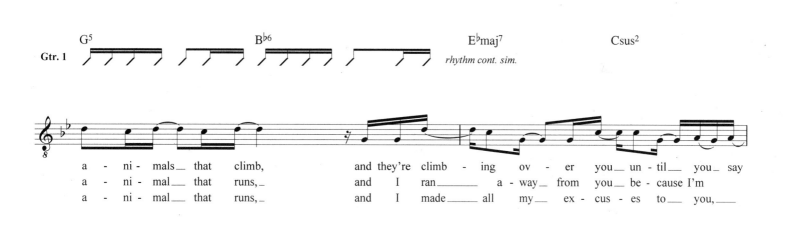

Gtr. 1

G5   B♭6   E♭maj7   Csus2

rhythm cont. sim.

a - ni - mals_ that climb, and they're climb - ing ov - er you_ un - til_ you_ say
a - ni - mal_ that runs,_ and I ran_____ a - way_ from you be - cause I'm
a - ni - mal_ that runs,_ and I made___ all my ex - cus - es to_ you,___

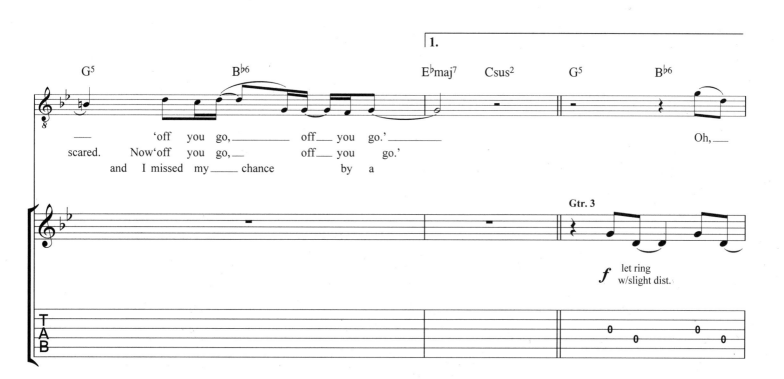

⌐1.

G5   B♭6   E♭maj7 Csus2   G5   B♭6

___ 'off you go,_____ off_ you go.' _____ Oh,___
scared. Now 'off you go,_ off_ you go.'
and I missed my_ chance by a

Gtr. 3

f let ring
w/slight dist.

```
T
A
B
```

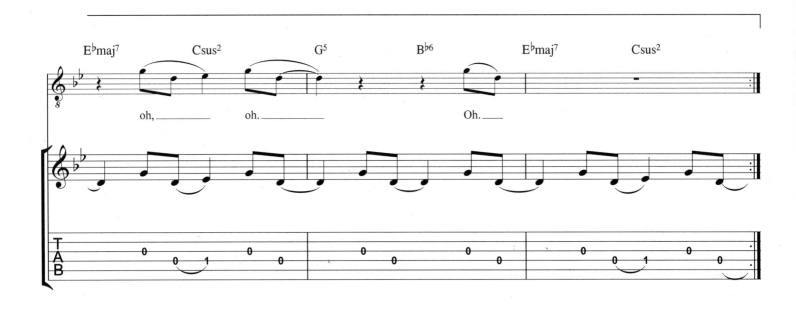

oh,_____ oh._____ Oh._____

2.3.

Chorus

stone's_____ throw._____

But if you're gon-na___ go, go___ now._____

Gtr. 2 (Elec.)

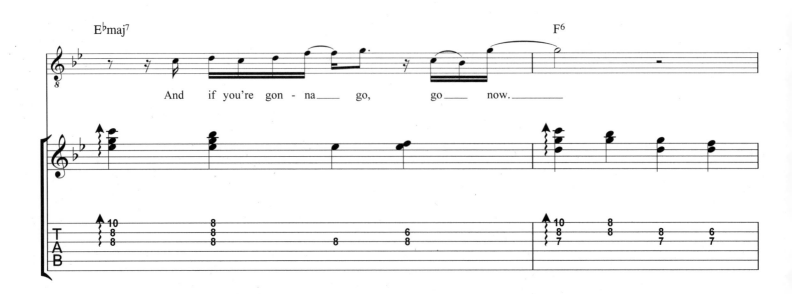

And if you're gon-na___ go, go___ now._____

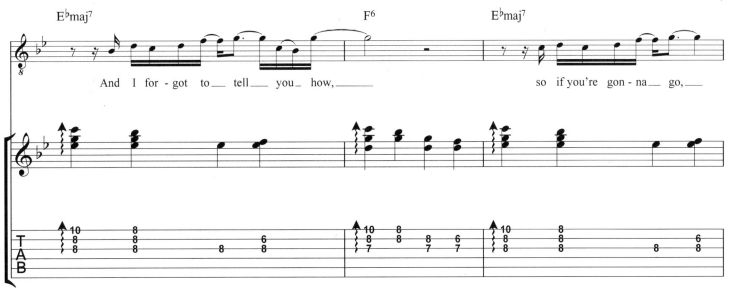

And I for - got to__ tell__ you__ how,_____ so if you're gon - na__ go,___

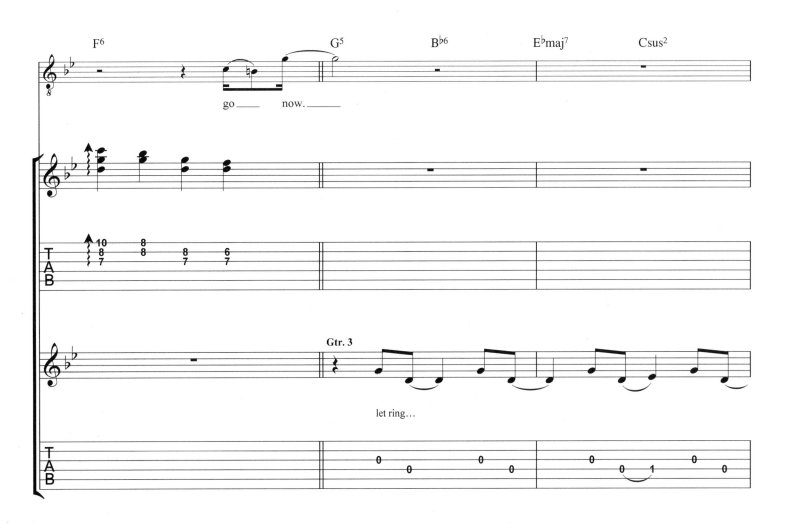

go____ now._____

Gtr. 3

let ring…

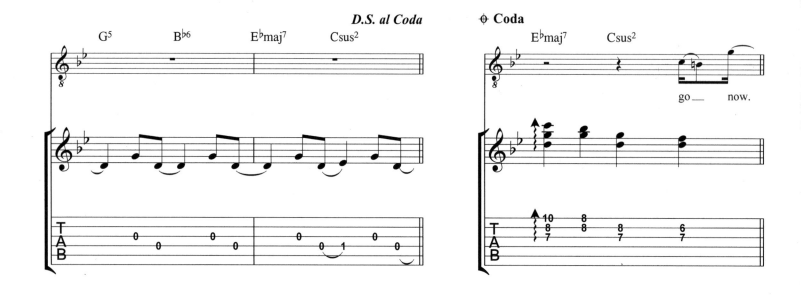

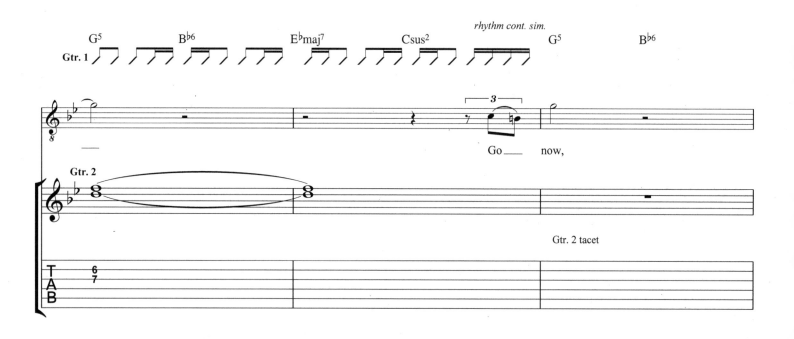

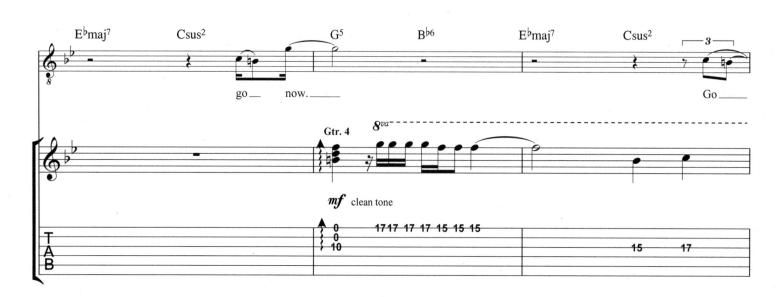

BROTHERS AND SISTERS

Words & Music by
Guy Berryman, Jon Buckland, Will Champion & Chris Martin

Capo 2nd fret

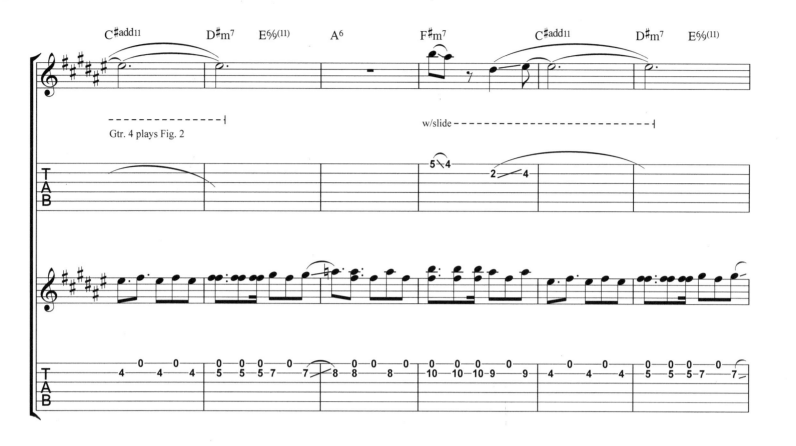

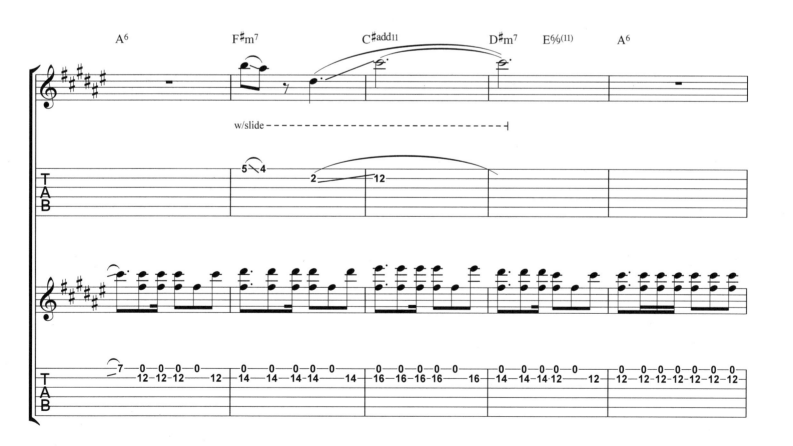

15

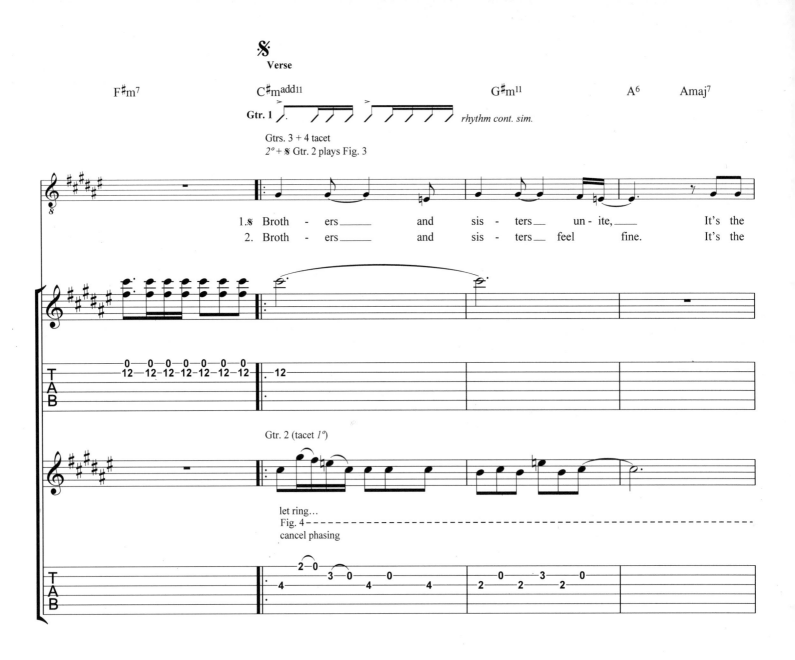

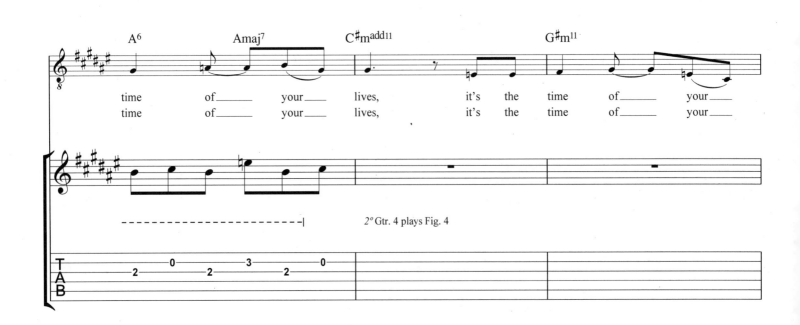

But just stay down,

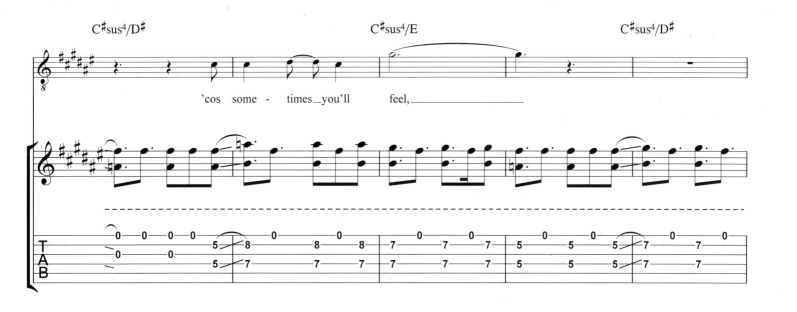

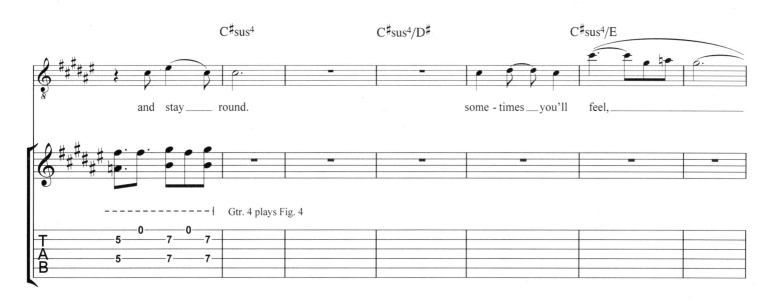

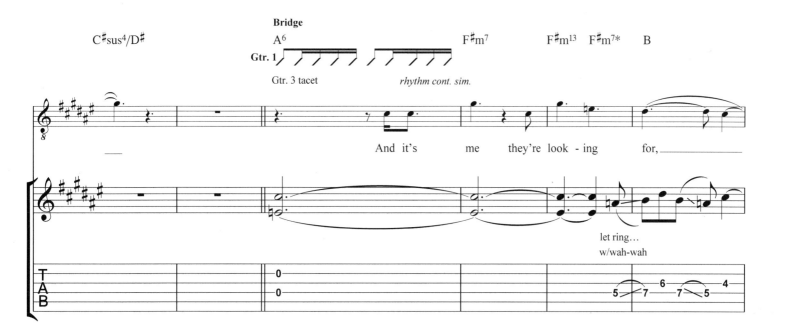

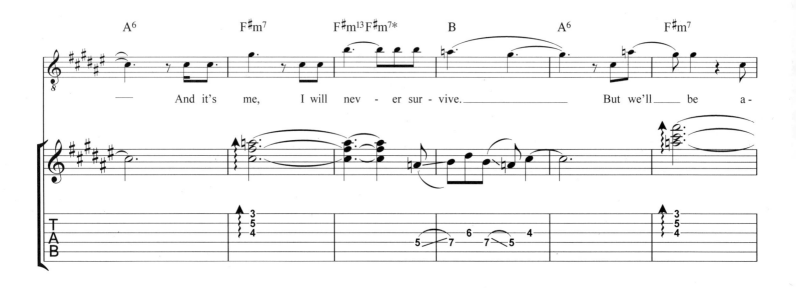

And it's me, I will nev - er sur - vive._____ But we'll_____ be a-

To Coda D.S. al Coda

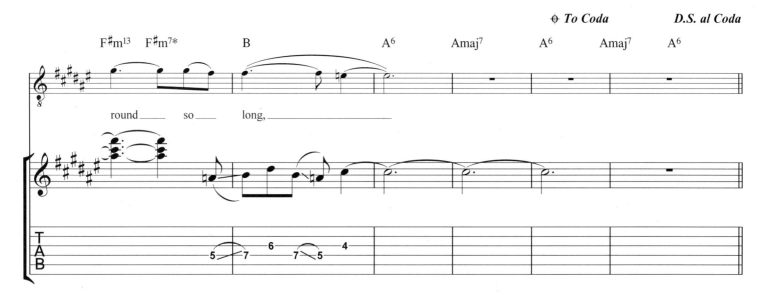

round_____ so_____ long,_____

Coda

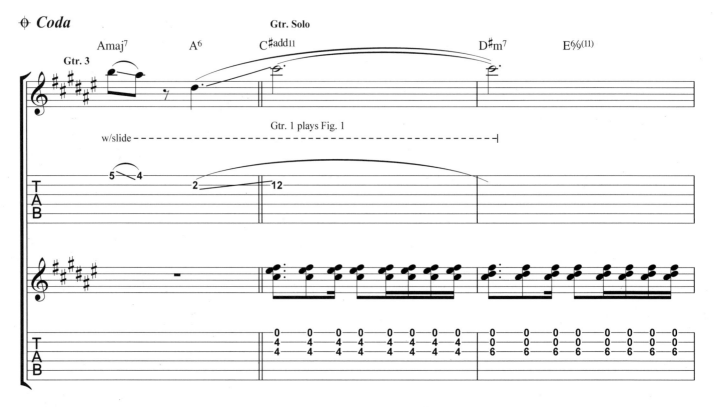

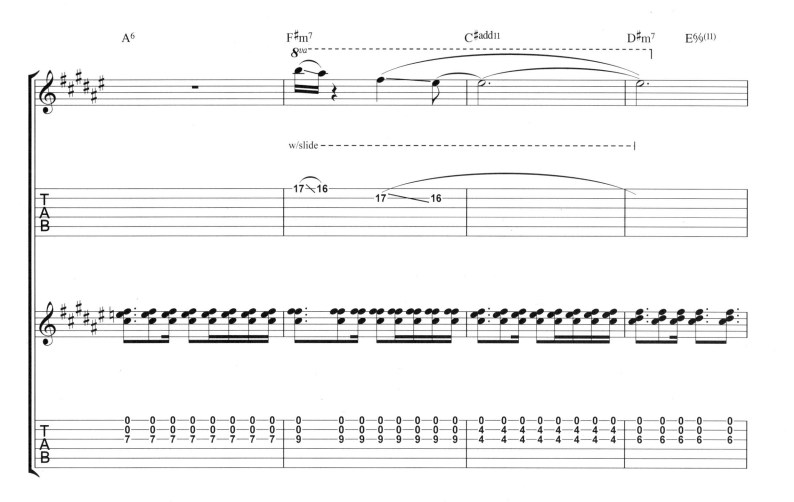

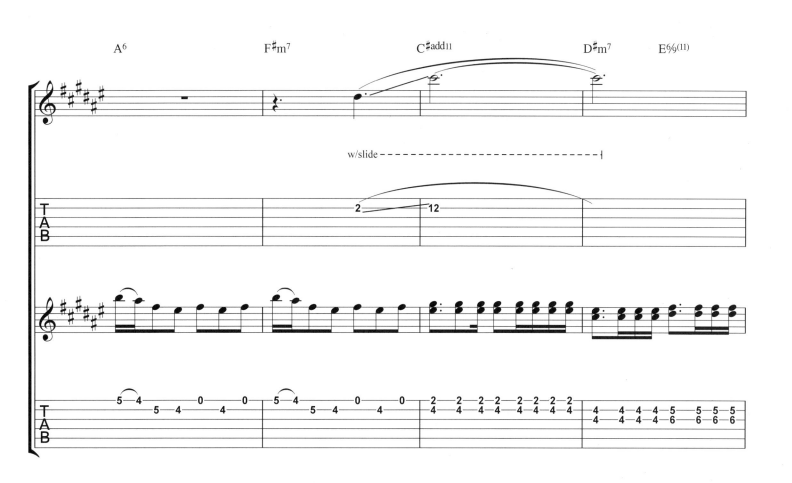

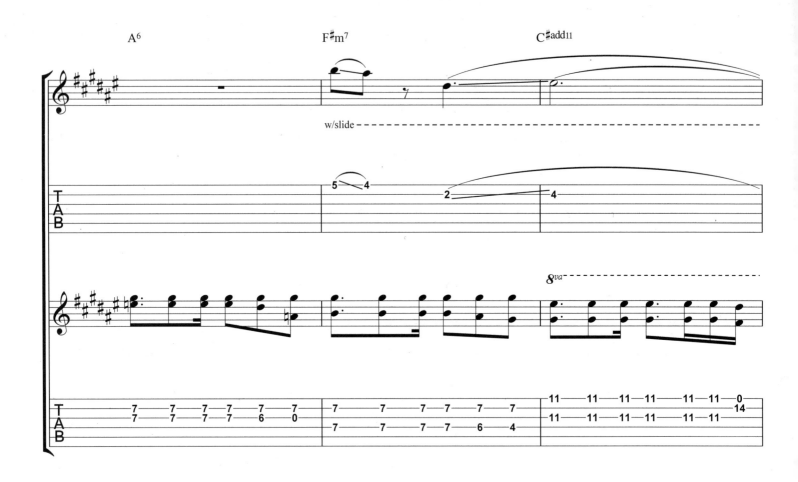

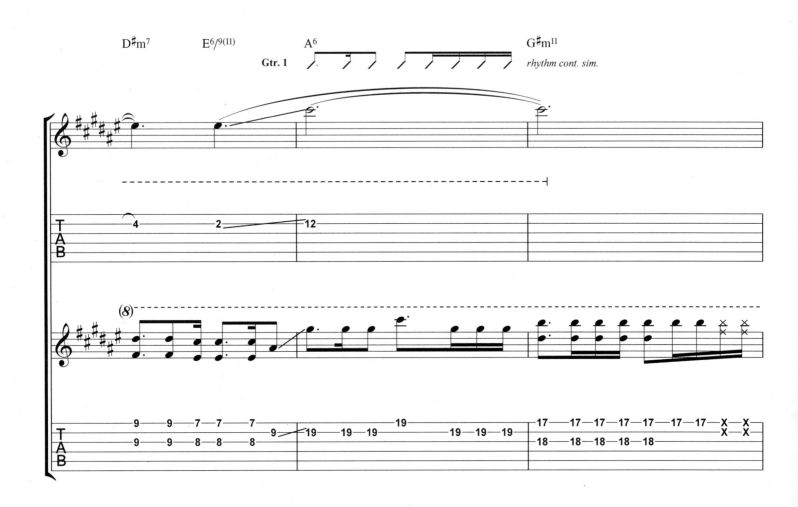

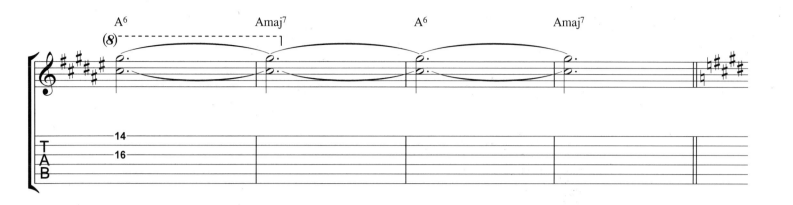

Outro

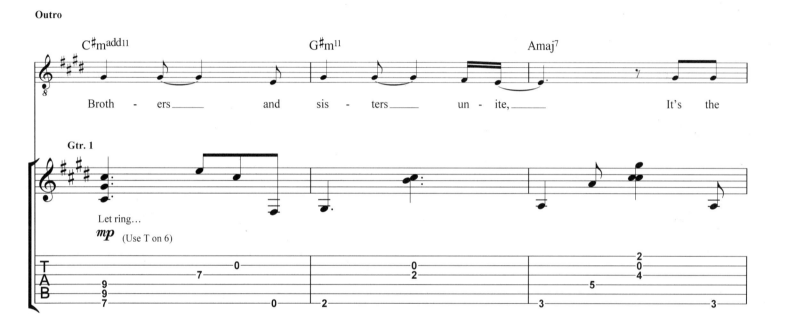

Broth - ers _____ and sis - ters _____ un - ite, _____ It's the

time of _____ your _____ lives, it's the time of _____ your _____ lives.

BIGGER STRONGER

Words & Music by
Guy Berryman, Jon Buckland, Will Champion & Chris Martin

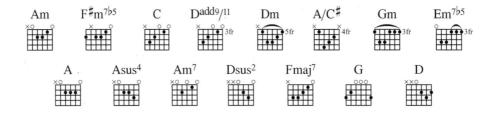

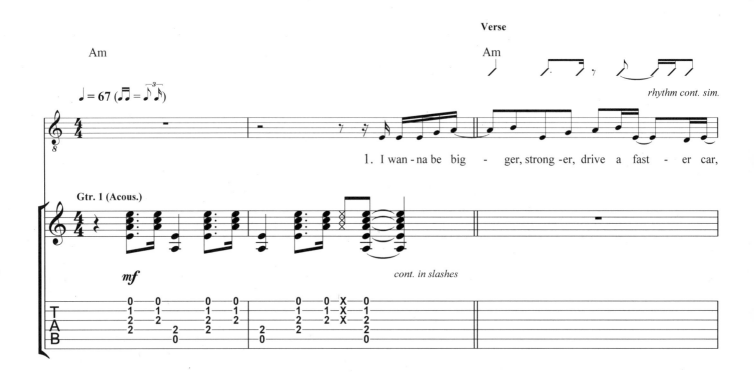

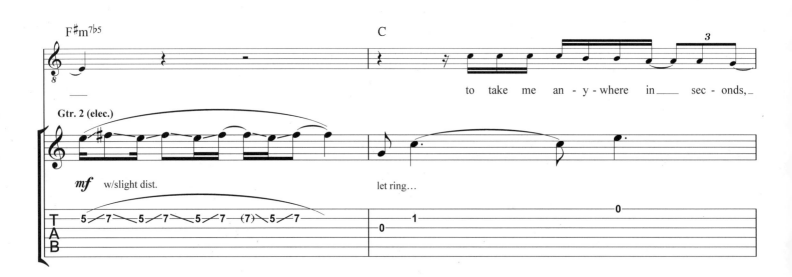

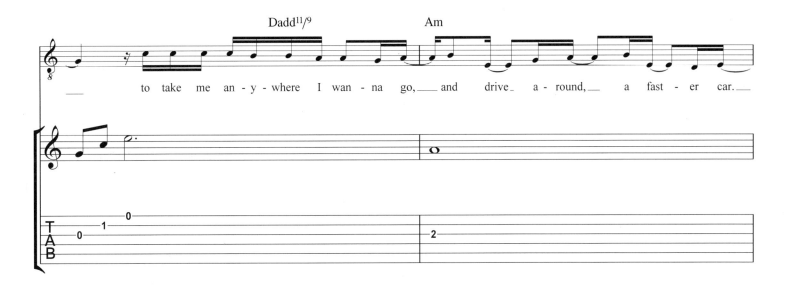

to take me an-y-where I wan-na go,___ and drive___ a-round,___ a fast-er car.___

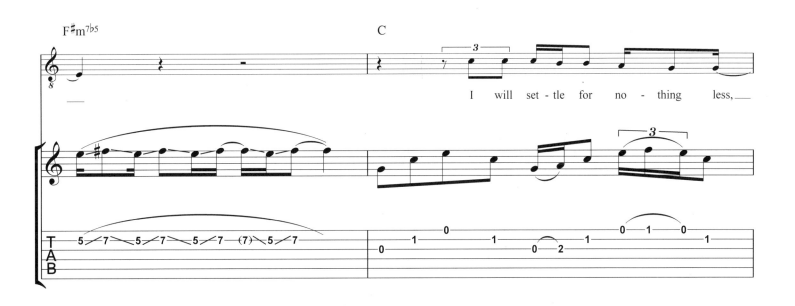

I will set-tle for no-thing less,___

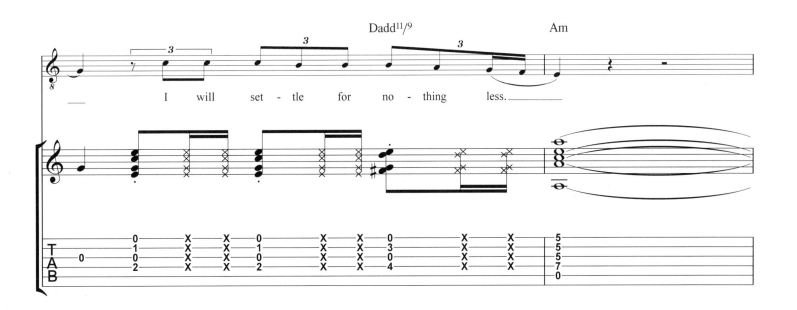

I will set-tle for no-thing less.___

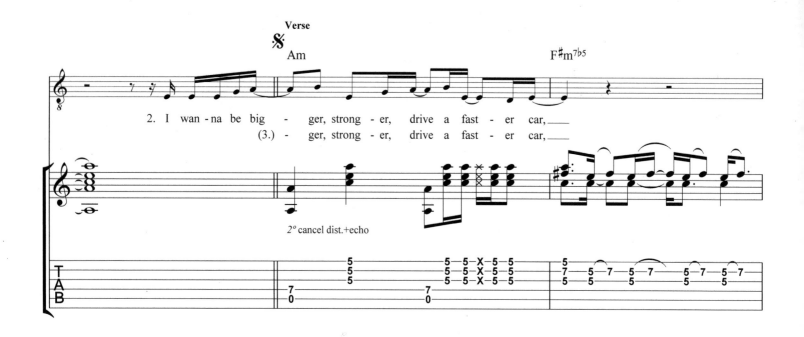

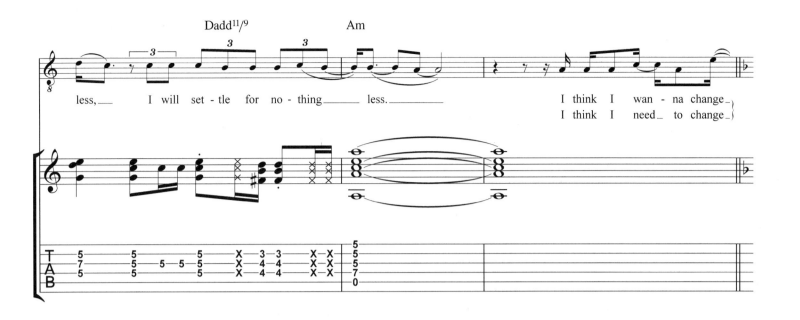

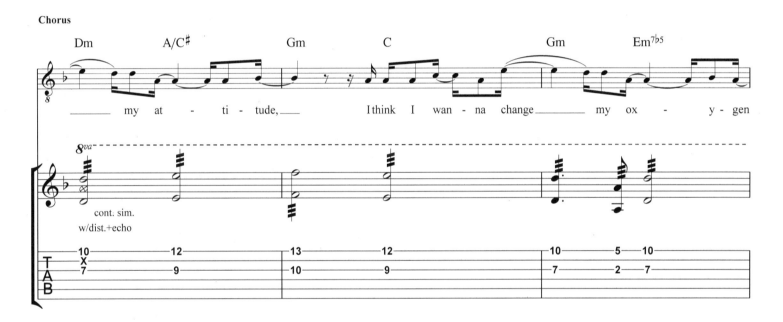

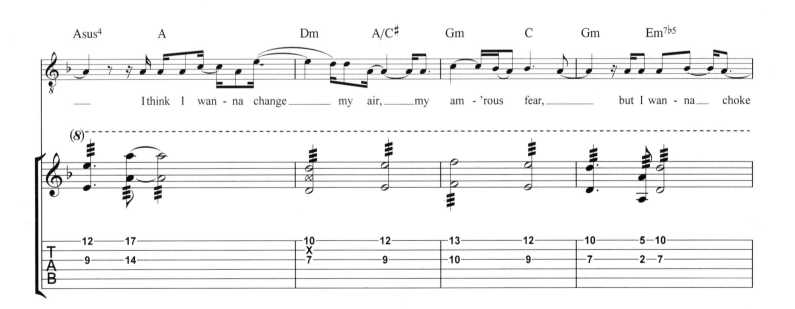

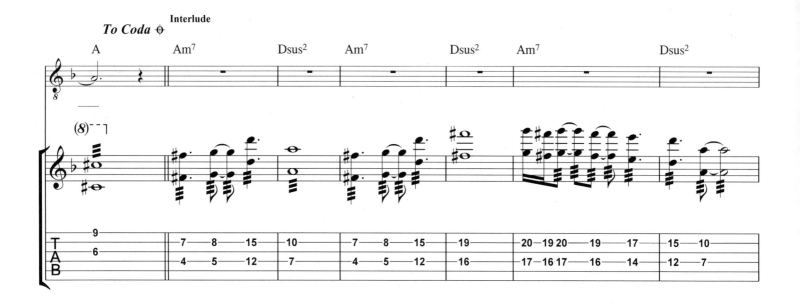

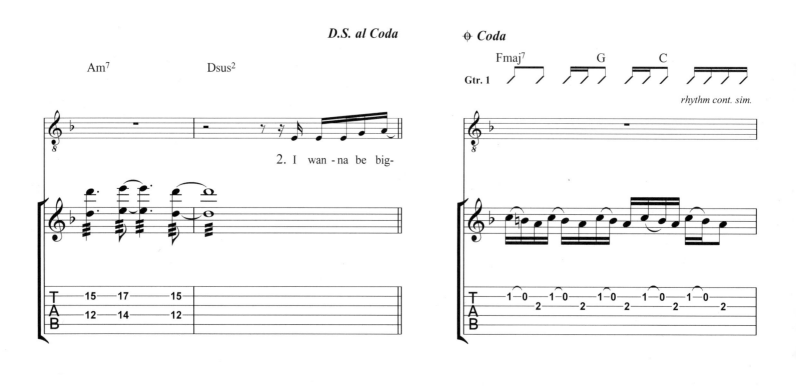

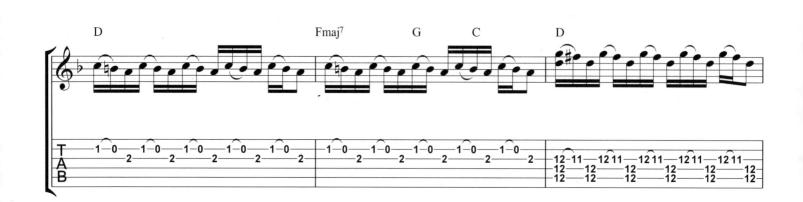

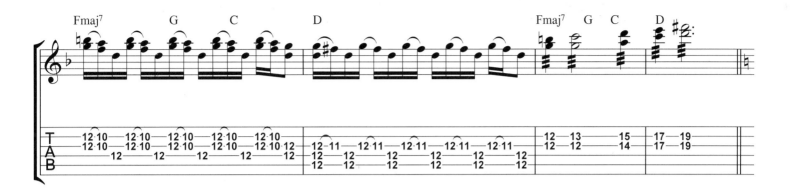

Interlude

w/chorus

full

cont. ad lib

rhythm cont. sim.

Bridge

Outro

Big - ger____ and bet - ter,   Big - ger____ and bet - ter,   Big - ger, strong - er, drive a fast - er car,____

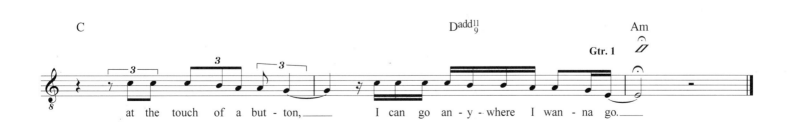

at the touch of a but - ton,____   I can go an - y - where I wan - na go.____

CAREFUL WHERE YOU STAND

Words & Music by
Guy Berryman, Jon Buckland, Will Champion & Chris Martin

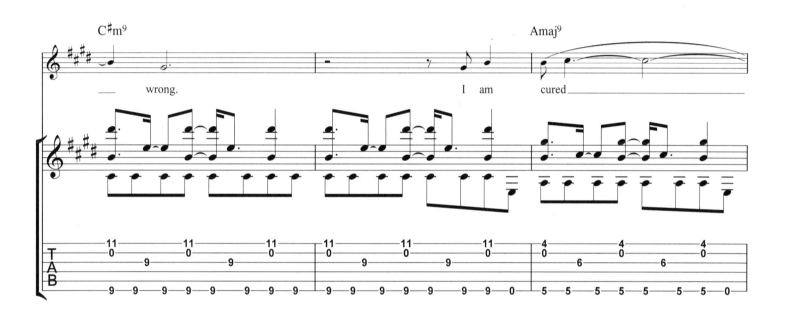

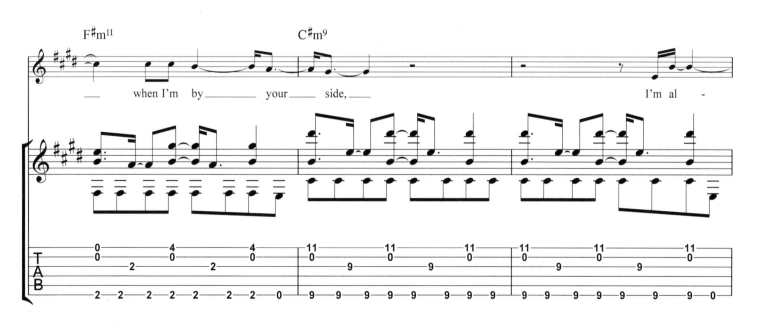

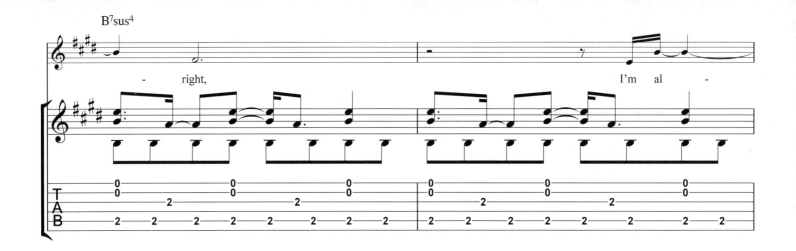

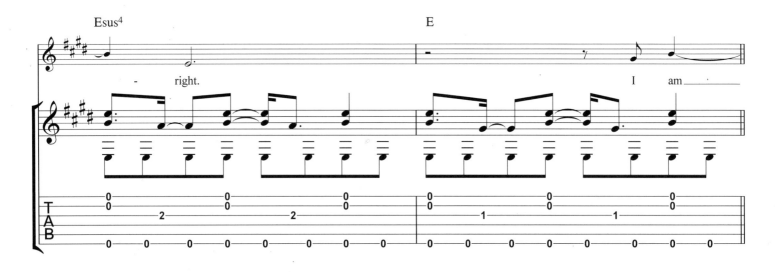

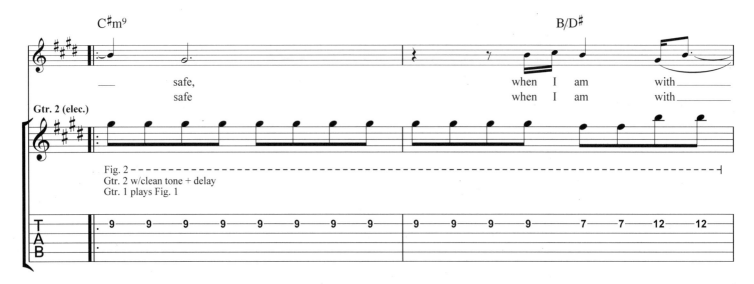

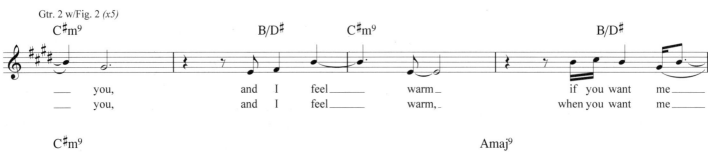

when I'm by your side, I'm al - right.
when you are a - round, I'm al - right.

And

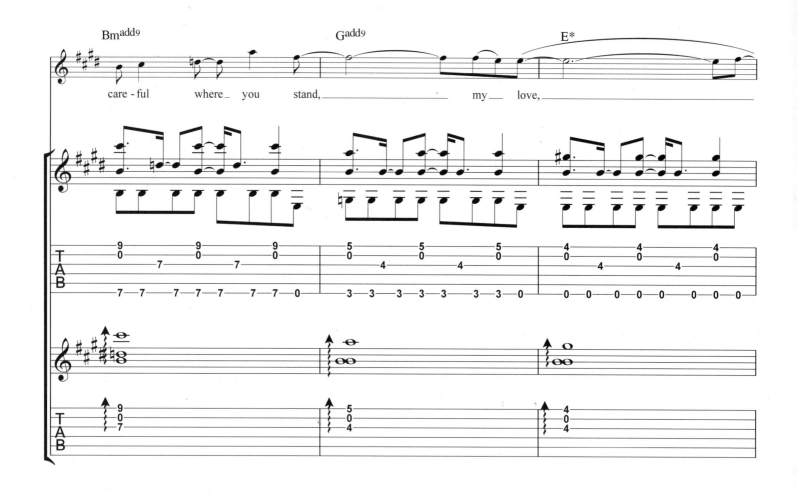

care-ful where you stand, my love,

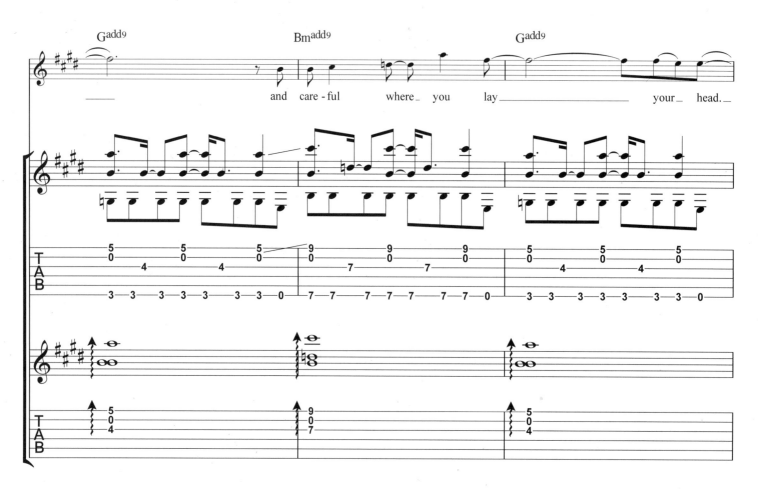

and care-ful where you lay your head.

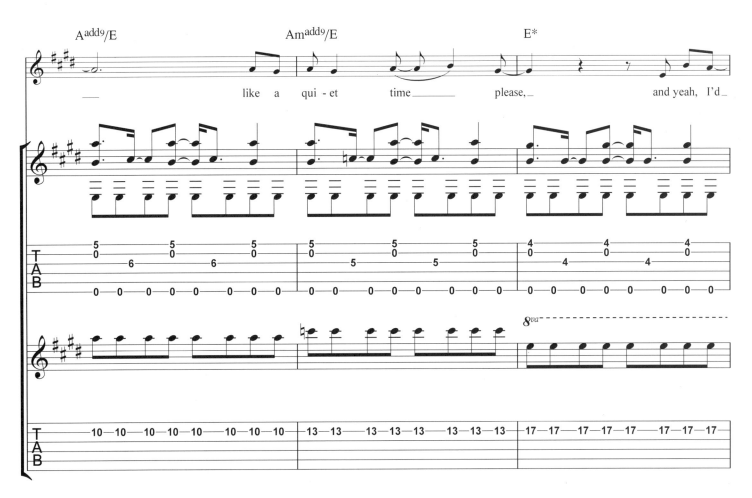

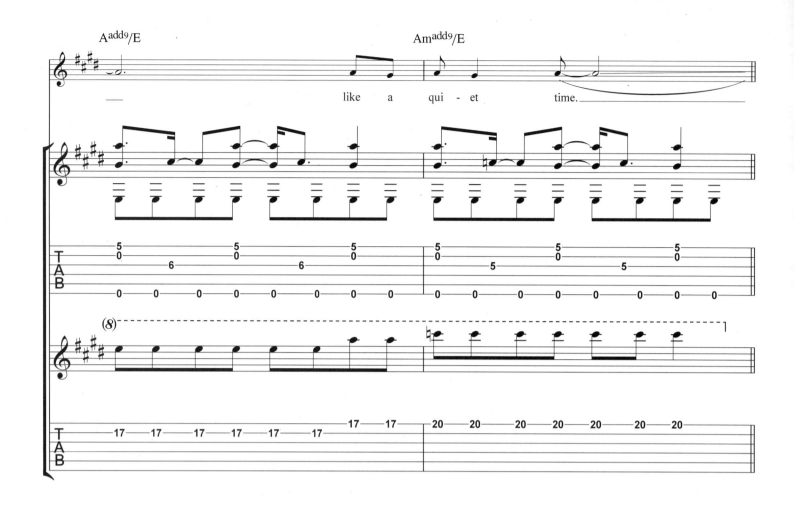

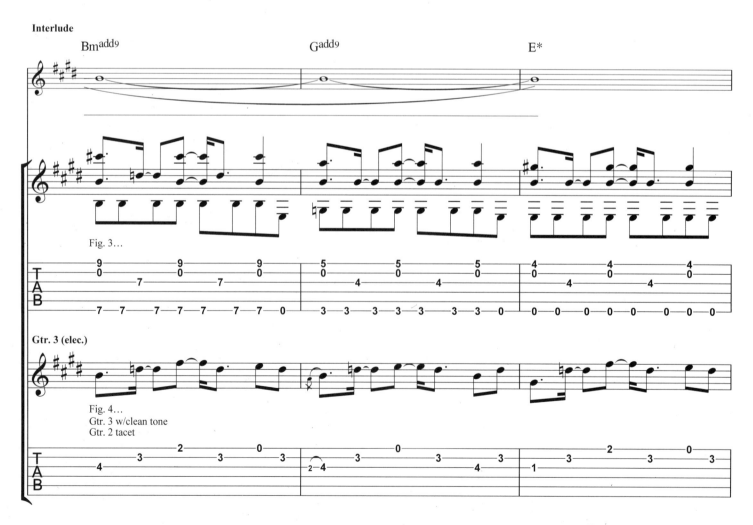

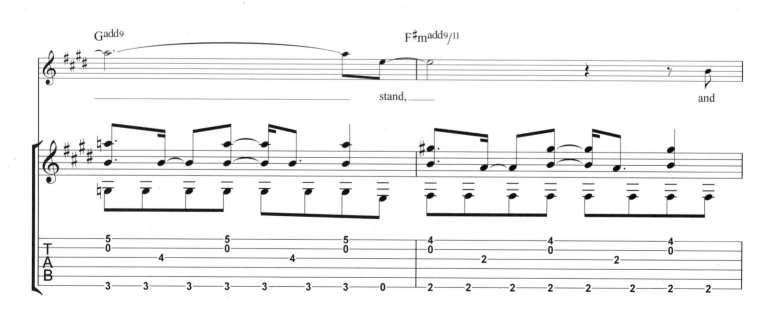

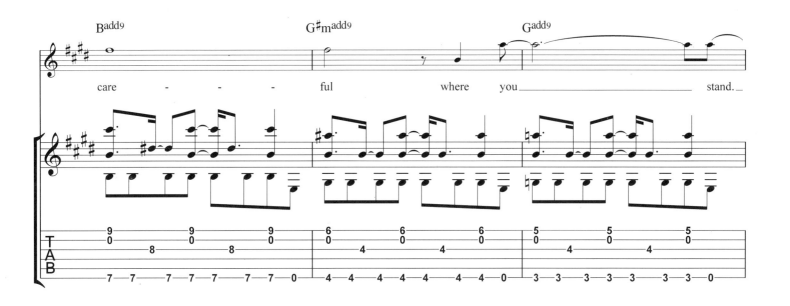

care - - - ful where you_____ stand._

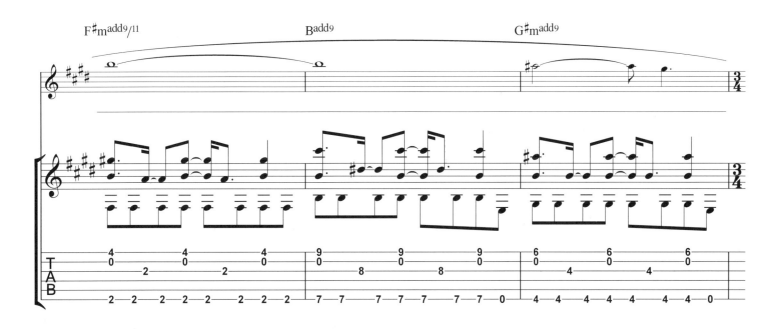

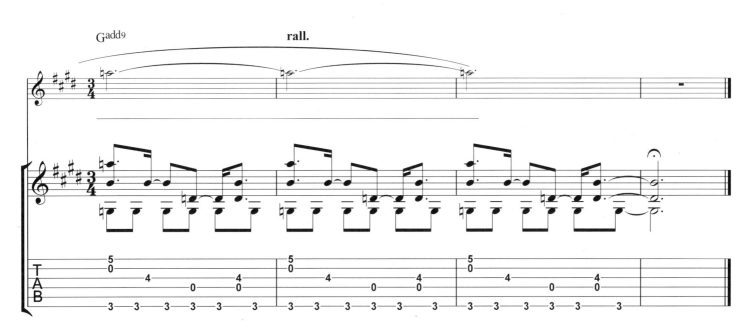

CLOCKS

Words & Music by
Guy Berryman, Jon Buckland, Will Champion & Chris Martin

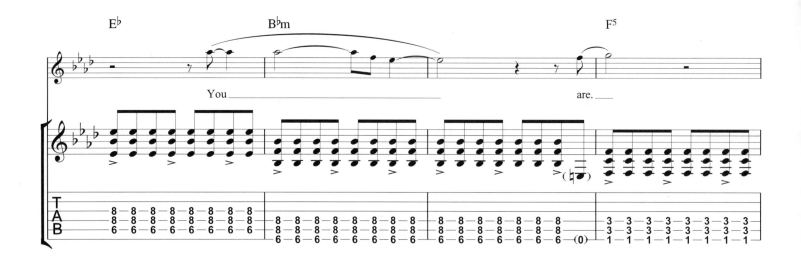

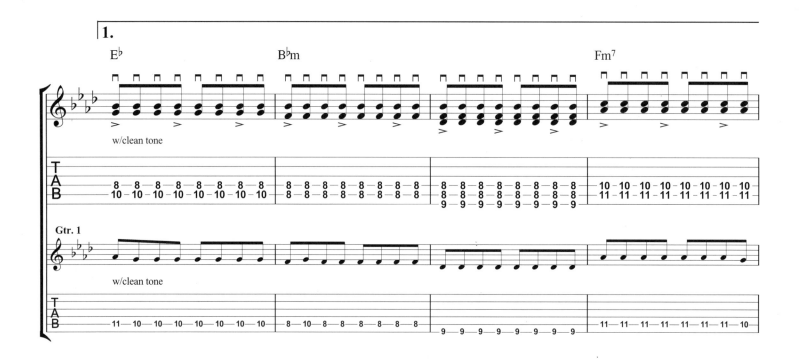

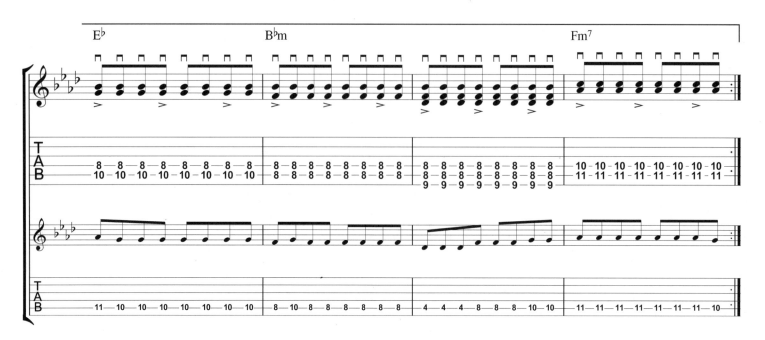

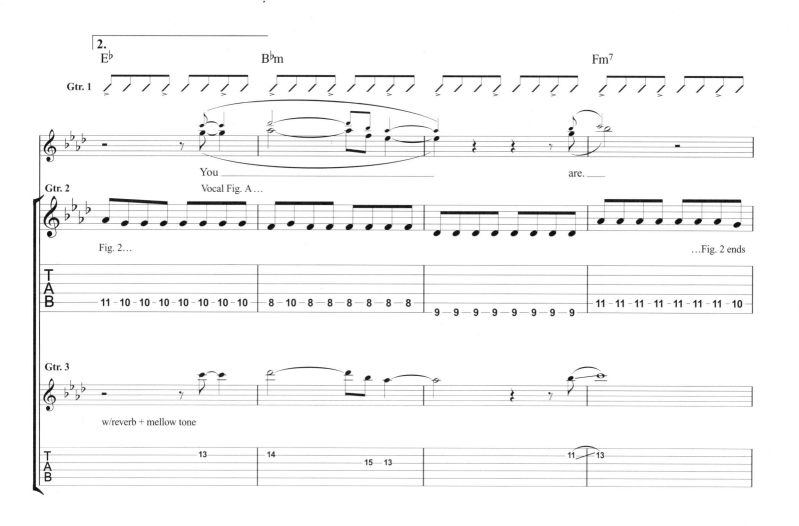

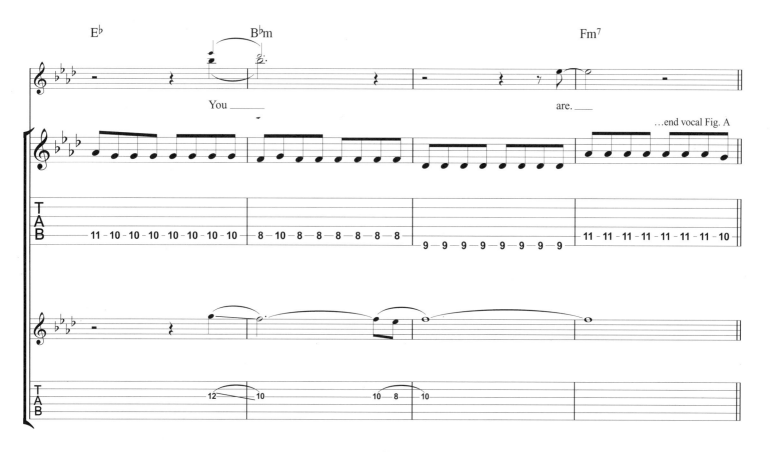

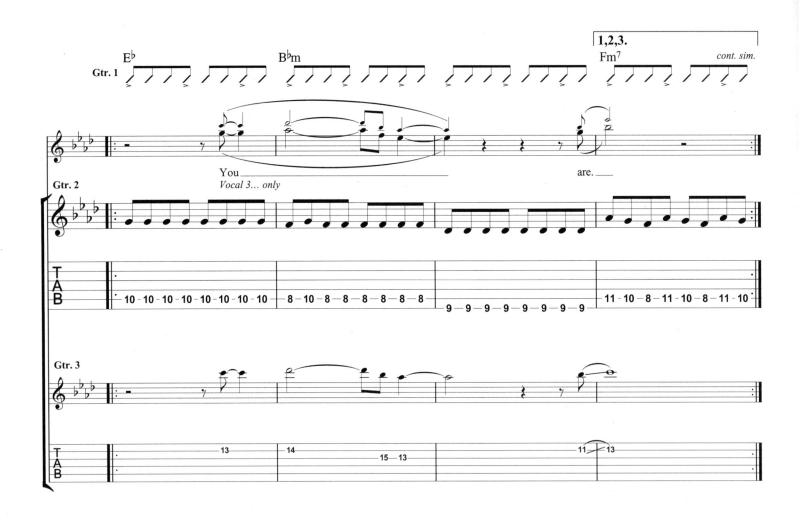

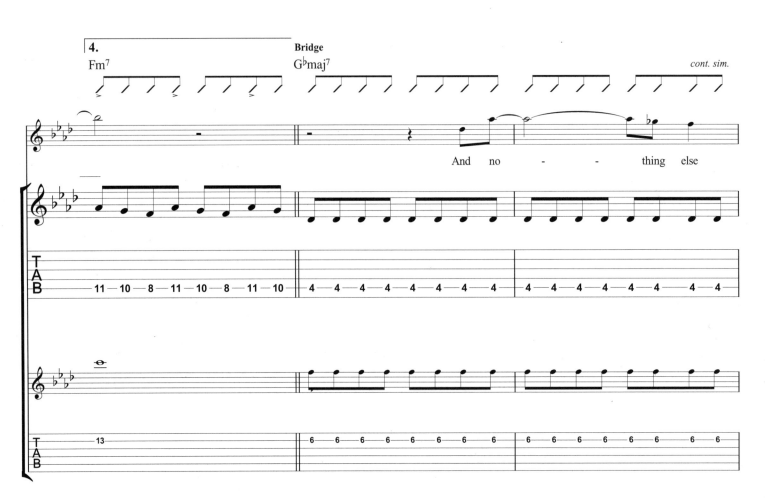

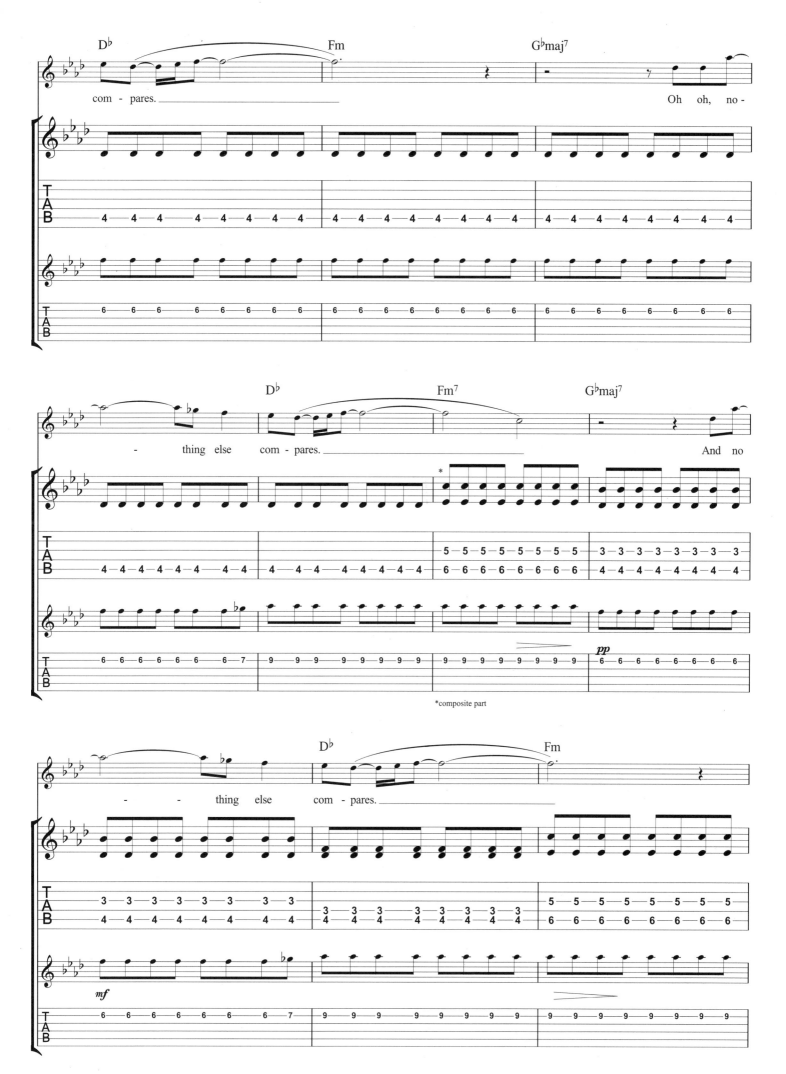

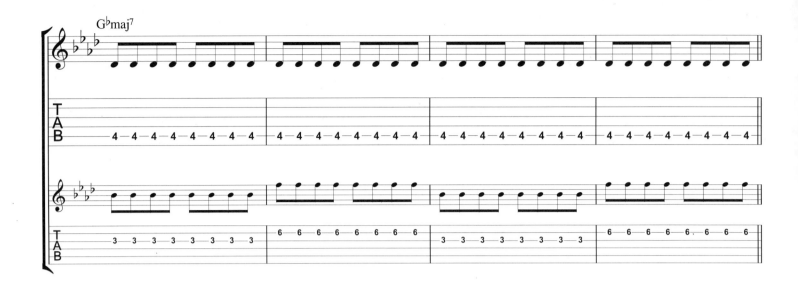

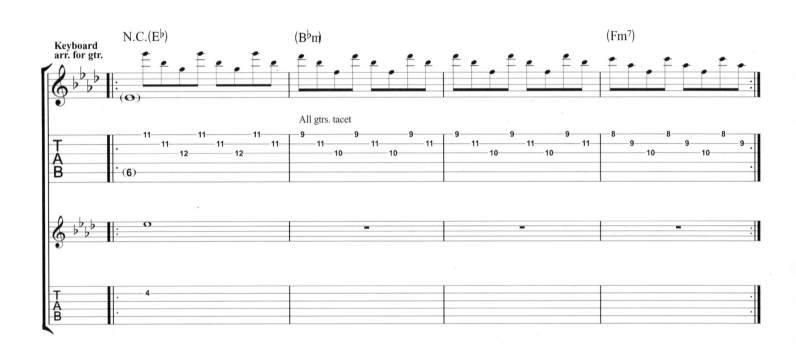

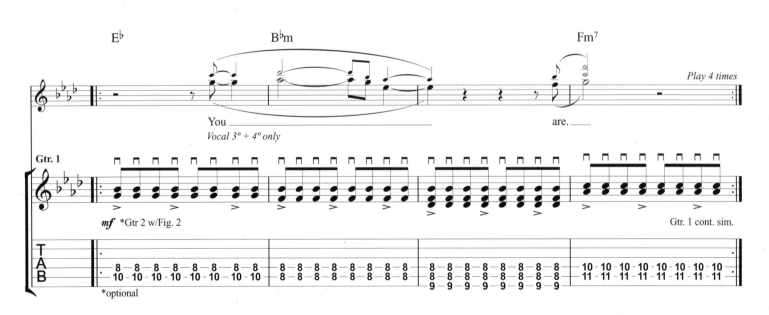

48

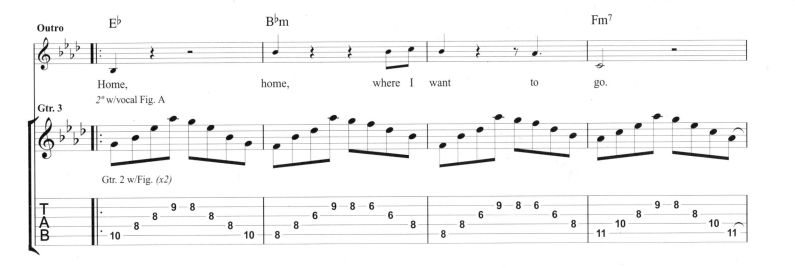

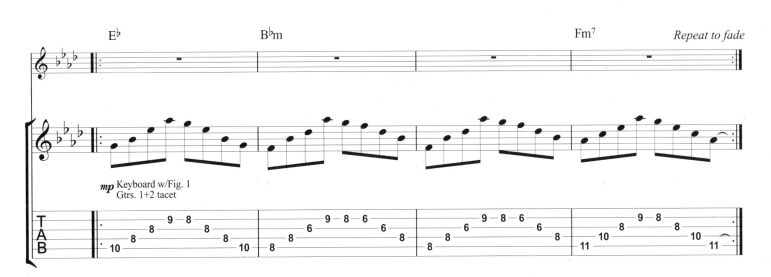

CRESTS OF WAVES

Words & Music by
Guy Berryman, Jon Buckland, Will Champion & Chris Martin

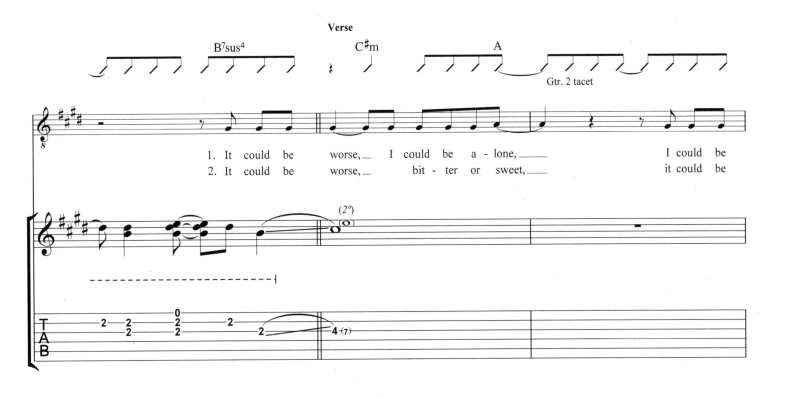

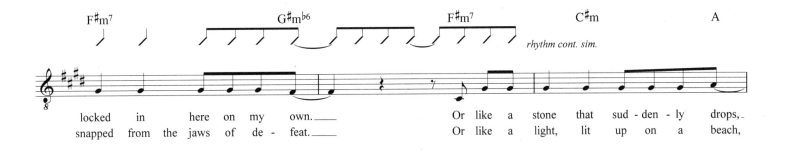

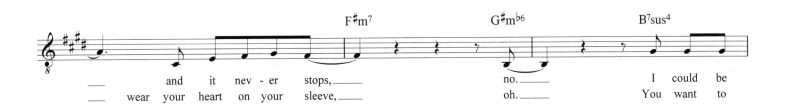

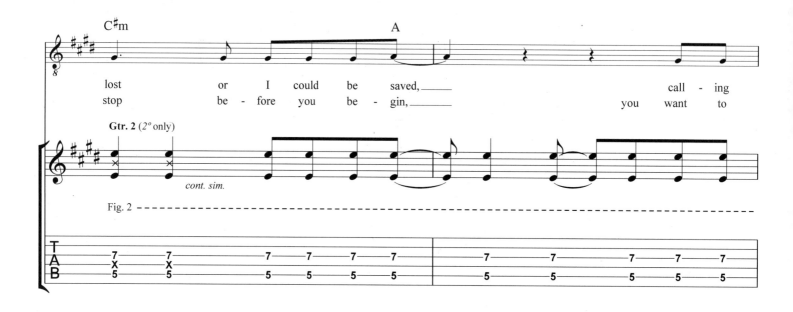

lost   or   I   could   be   saved,_____   call - ing
stop   be - fore   you   be - gin,_____   you   want   to

Gtr. 2 (*2° only*)

cont. sim.

Fig. 2 -

out   from   be - neath   the   waves._____   Beat - en   down   by   this   o - cean   rain,
sink   when   you   know   you   can   swim._____   You   want   to   stop   just   be - fore   you   be - gin,_

2° Gtr. 2 plays Fig. 2

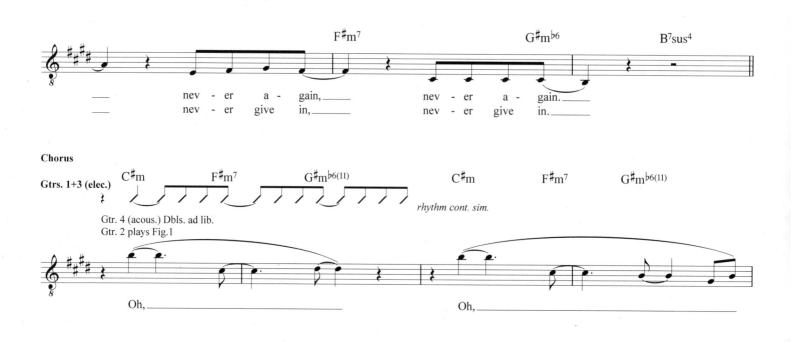

_____   nev - er   a - gain,_____   nev - er   a - gain._____
_____   nev - er   give   in,_____   nev - er   give   in._____

Chorus

Gtrs. 1+3 (elec.)

rhythm cont. sim.

Gtr. 4 (acous.) Dbls. ad lib.
Gtr. 2 plays Fig.1

Oh,_____   Oh,_____

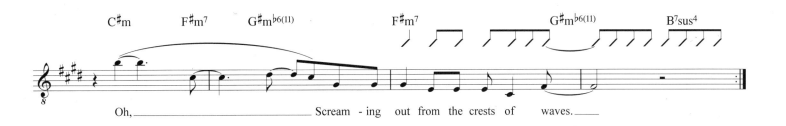

Oh, _____ Scream - ing out from the crests of waves. _____

Bridge

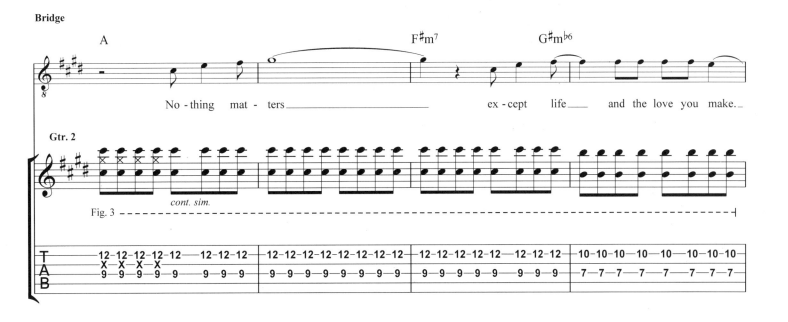

No - thing mat - ters _____ ex - cept life _____ and the love you make. _____

Gtr. 2

cont. sim.

Fig. 3 -

_____ No - thing mat - ters _____ ex - cept life _____ and the love you make. _____ No - thing mat -

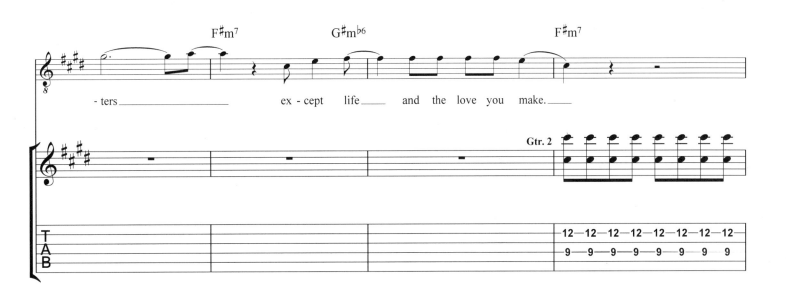

- ters _____ ex - cept life _____ and the love you make. _____

Gtr. 2

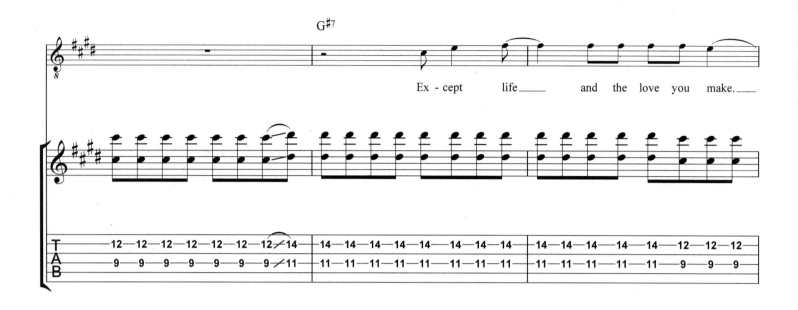

G#7

Ex - cept   life____   and   the   love   you   make.____

Chorus

Gtrs. 1,3+4

C#m   F#m7   G#m♭6(11)   C#m   F#m7   G#m♭6(11)

Gtr. 2 plays Fig. 1

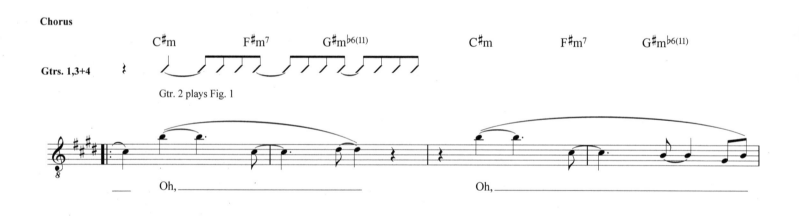

____   Oh,____   Oh,____

1.

C#m   F#m7   G#m♭6(11)   F#m7   G#m♭6(11)   B7sus4

Oh.____   Scream - ing   out   from   the   crests   of   waves.____

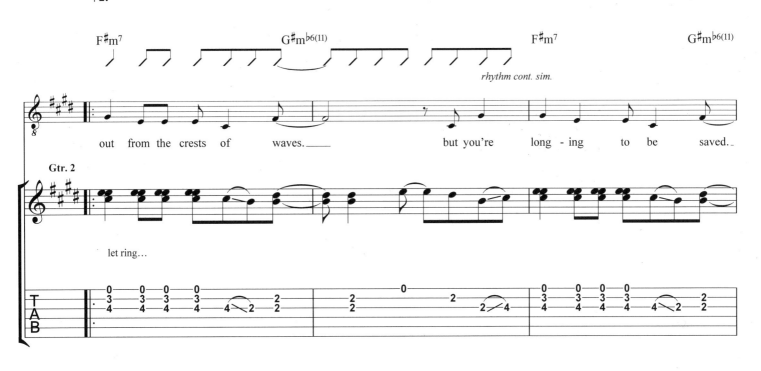

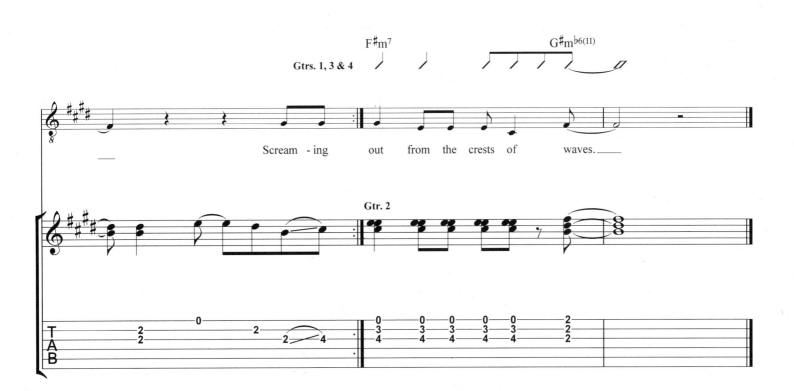

DON'T PANIC

Words & Music by
Guy Berryman, Jon Buckland, Will Champion & Chris Martin

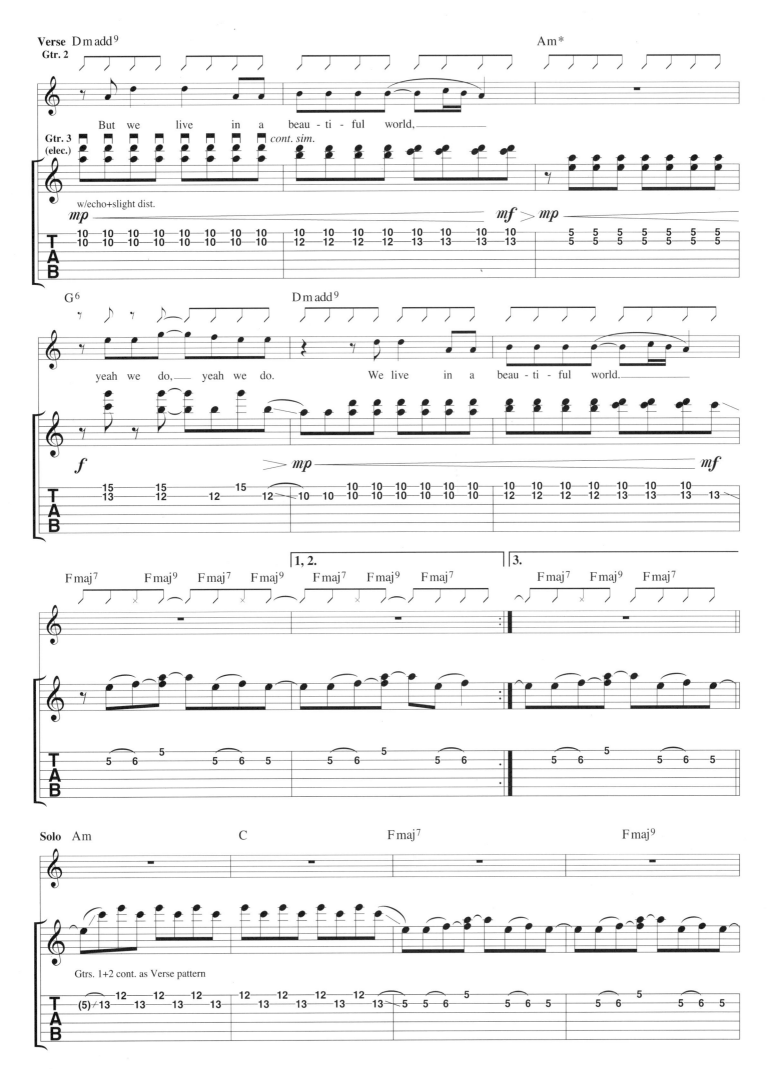

EASY TO PLEASE

Words & Music by
Guy Berryman, Jon Buckland, Will Champion & Chris Martin
Capo 2nd Fret

Capo 2nd fret = Tab 0. Chord names represent actual sounding chords

FIX YOU

Words & Music by
Guy Berryman, Jon Buckland, Will Champion & Chris Martin

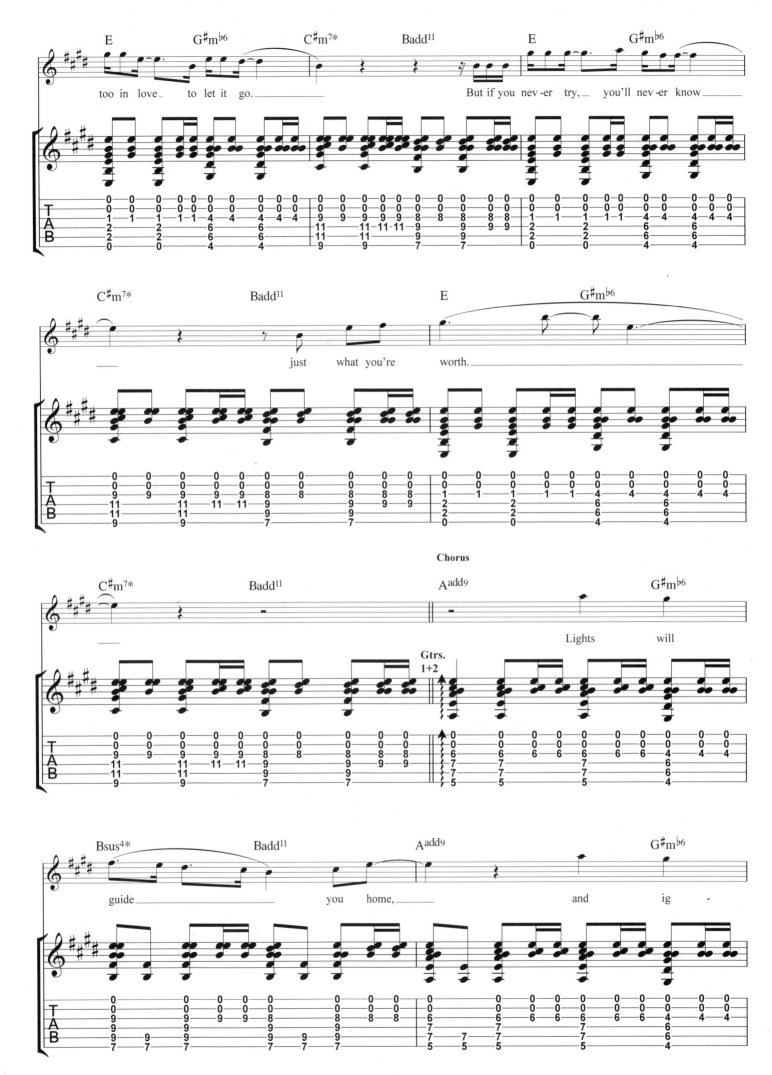

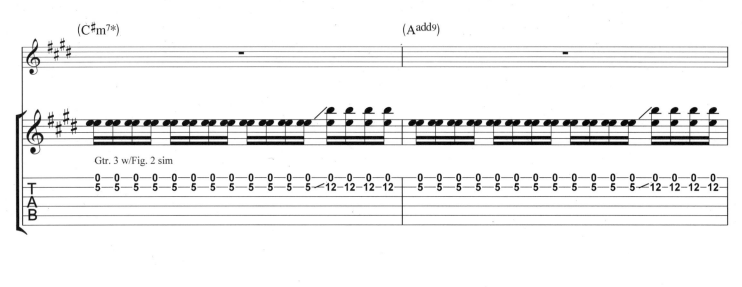

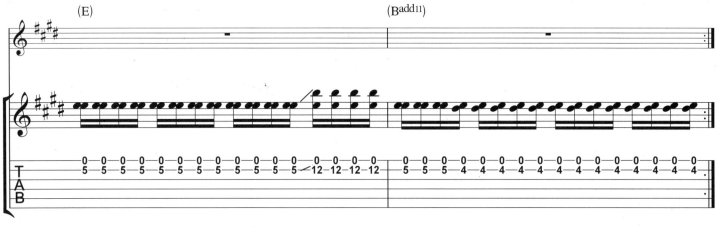

Bridge

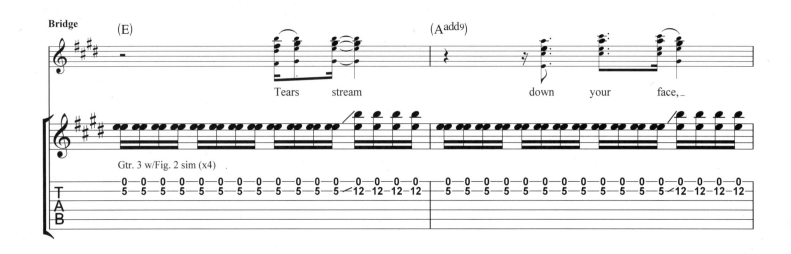

Tears   stream   down   your   face,_

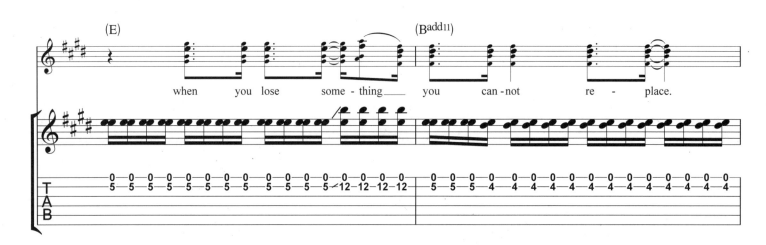

when   you   lose   some - thing____   you   can -not   re -   place.

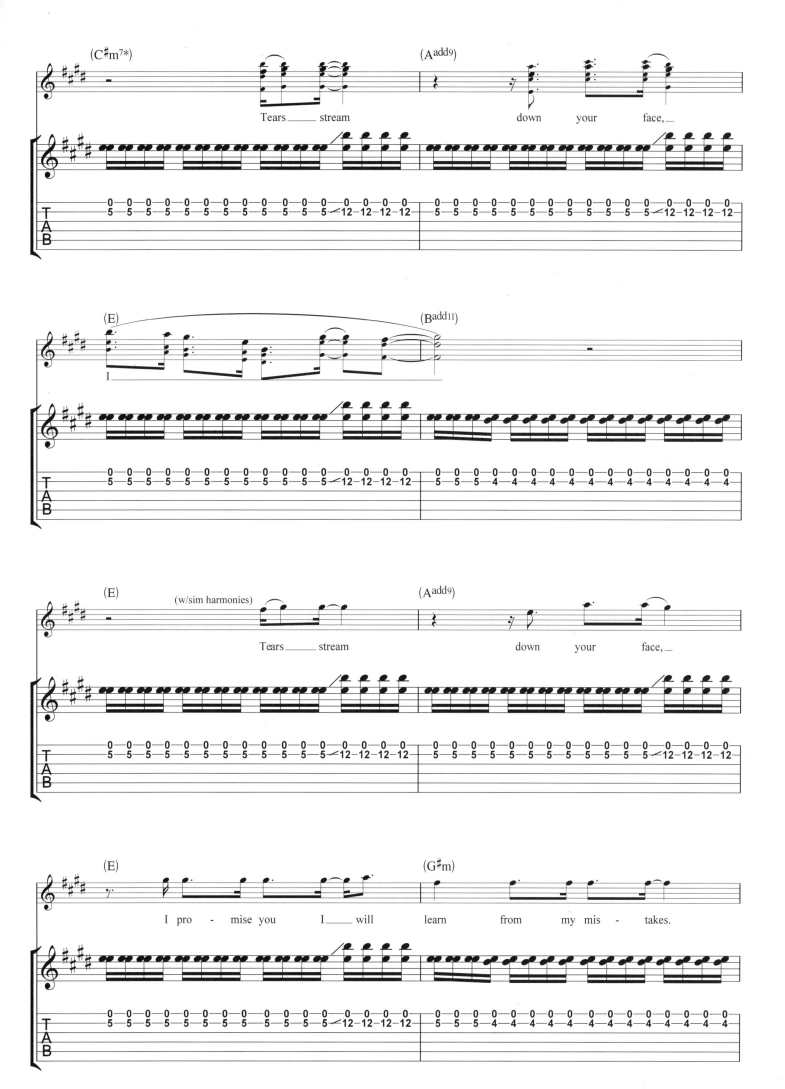

Outro

Lights will guide you home, and ig-nite your bones.

And I will try to fix you.

68

FOR YOU

Words & Music by
Guy Berryman, Jon Buckland, Will Champion & Chris Martin

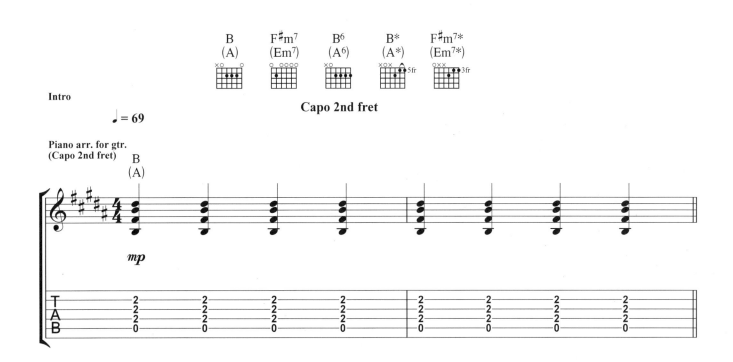

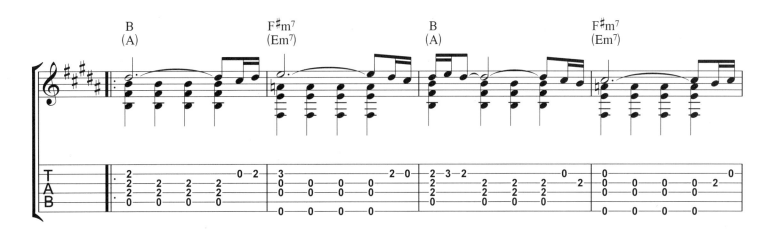

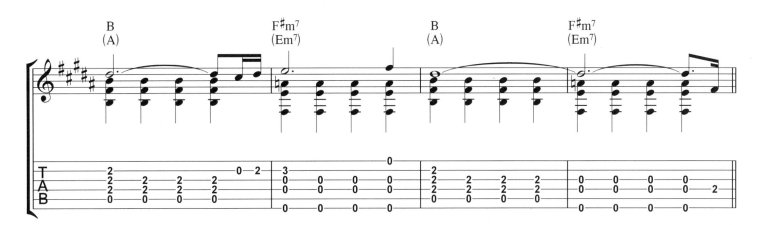

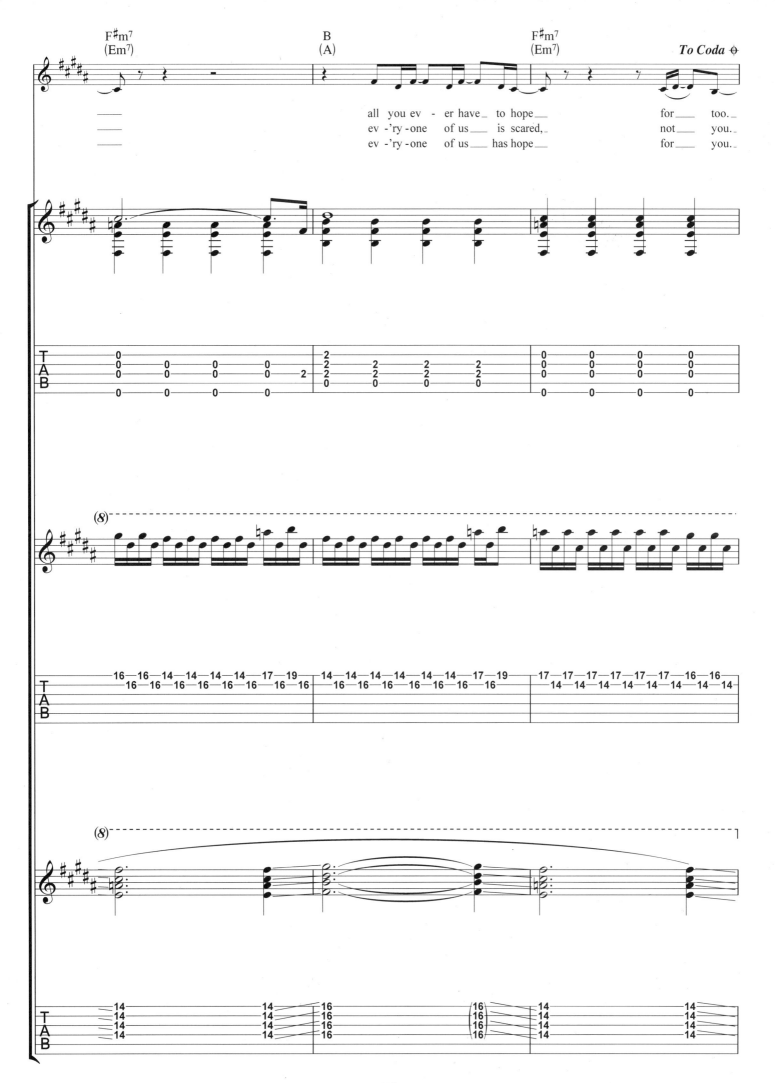

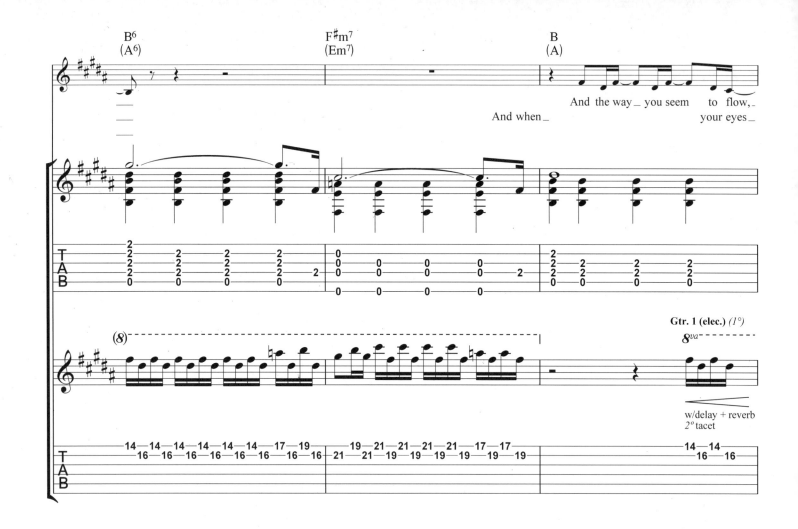

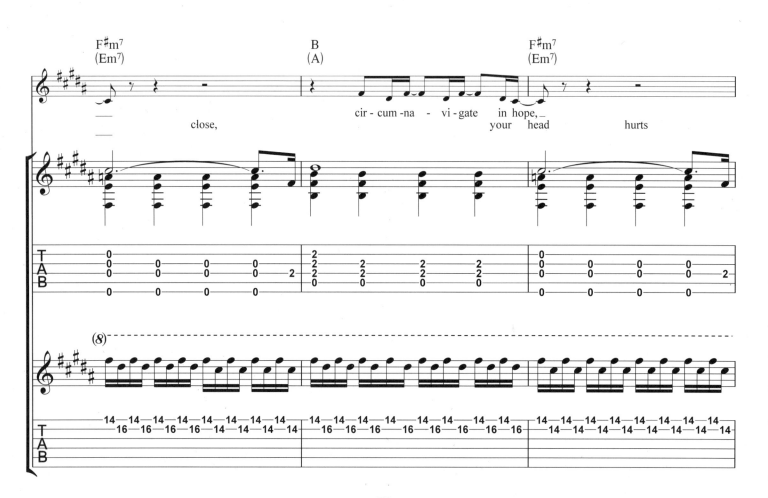

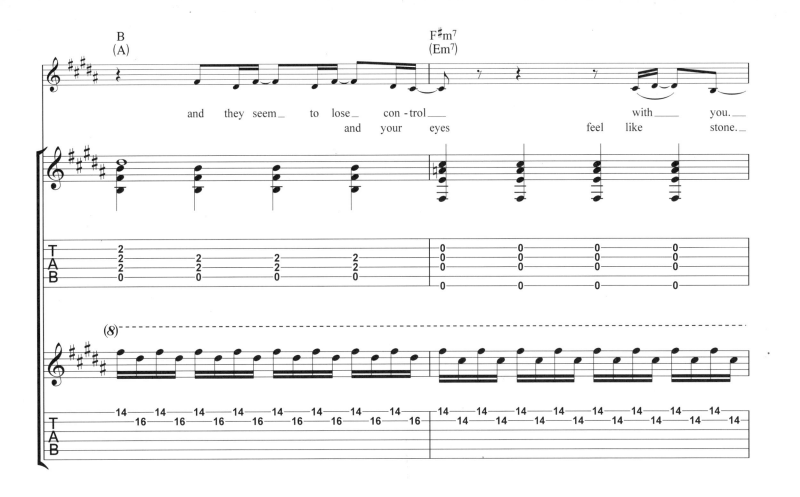

and they seem__ to lose__ con-trol__ with___ you.___
and your eyes feel like stone.___

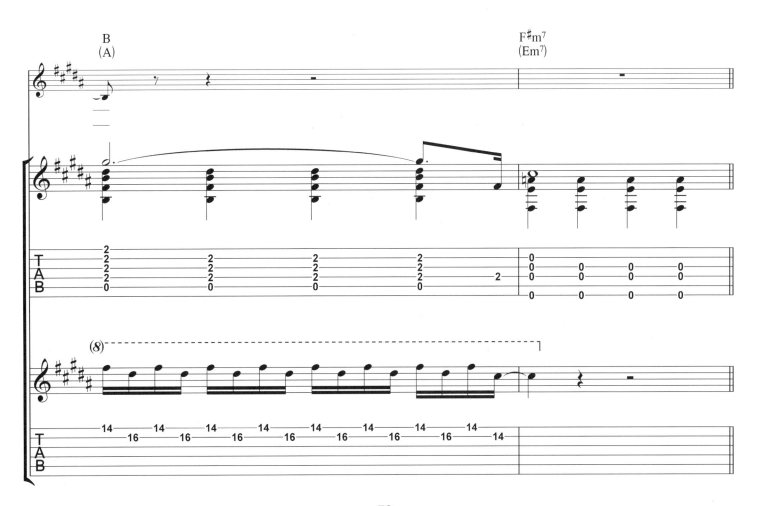

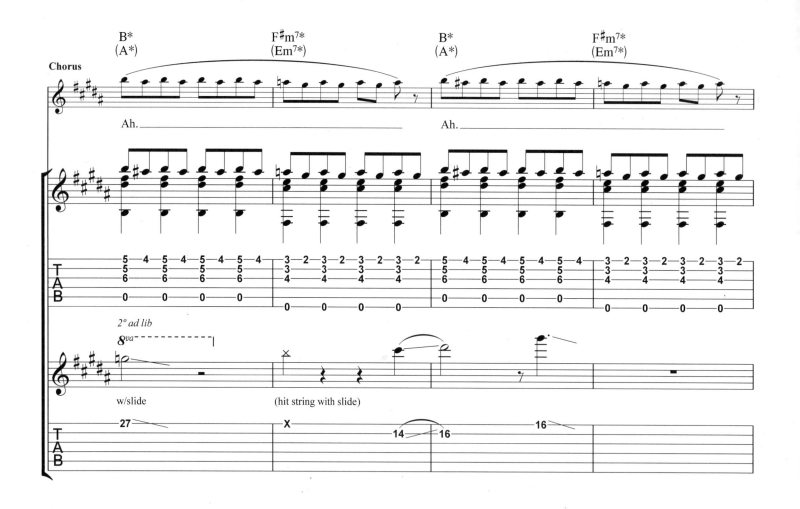

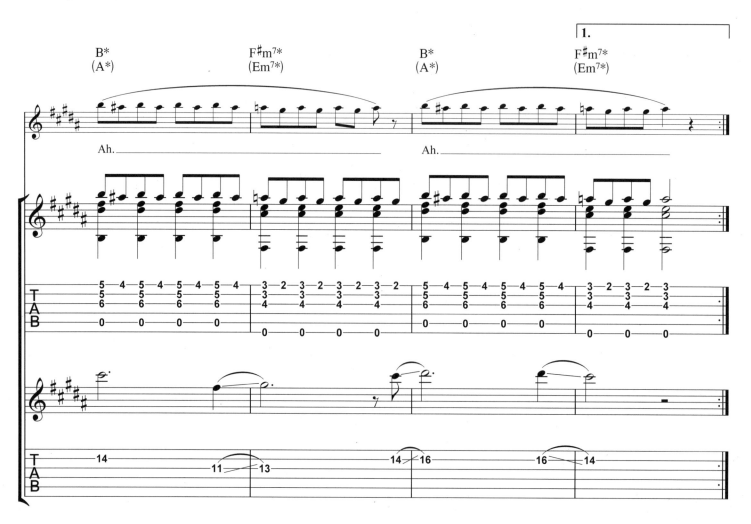

GOD PUT A SMILE UPON YOUR FACE

Words & Music by
Guy Berryman, Jon Buckland, Will Champion & Chris Martin

*basic chord names

1. Where do we go, no-bo-dy knows!

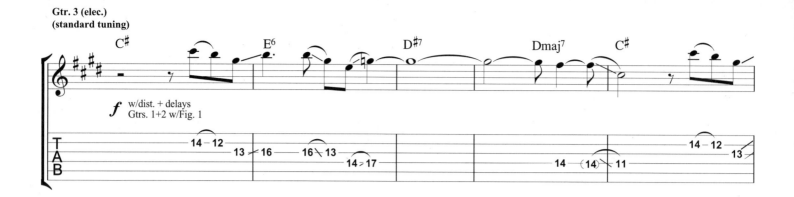

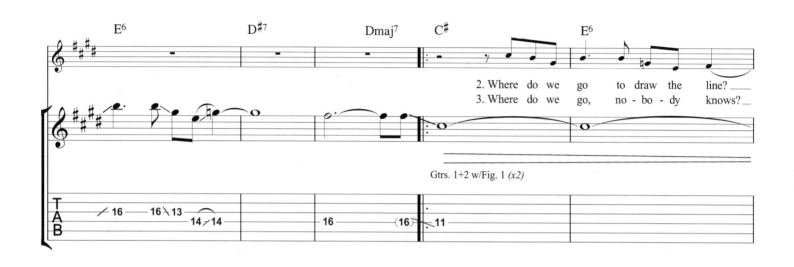

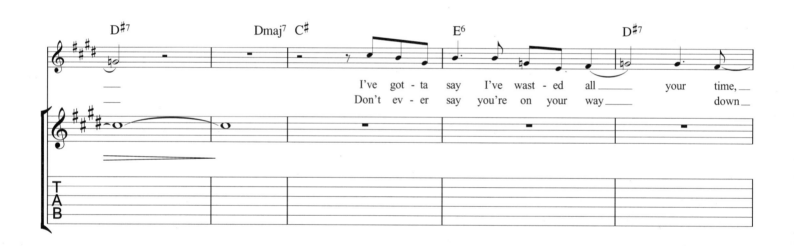

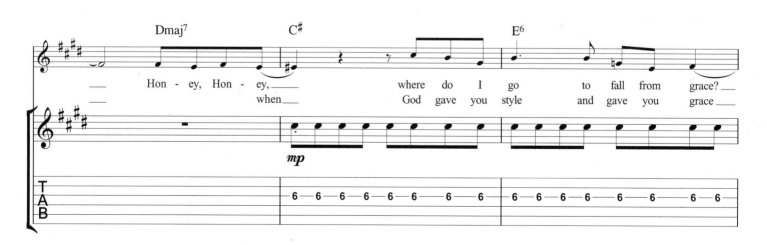

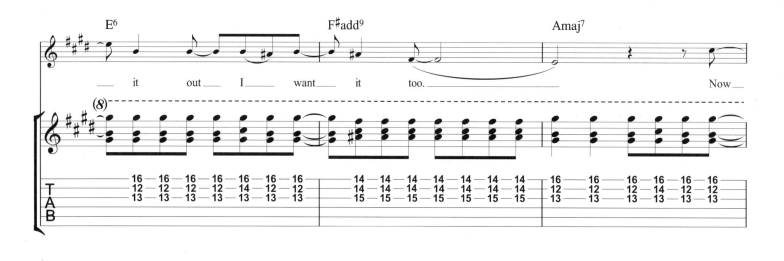

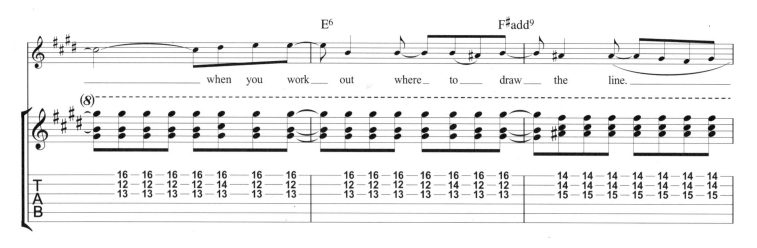

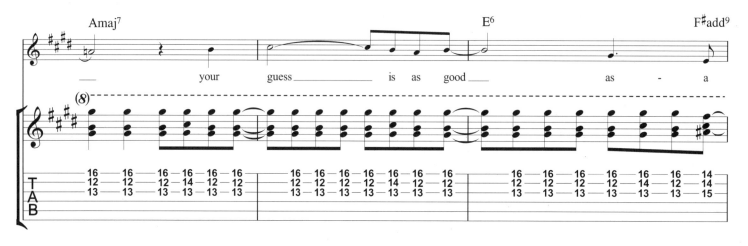

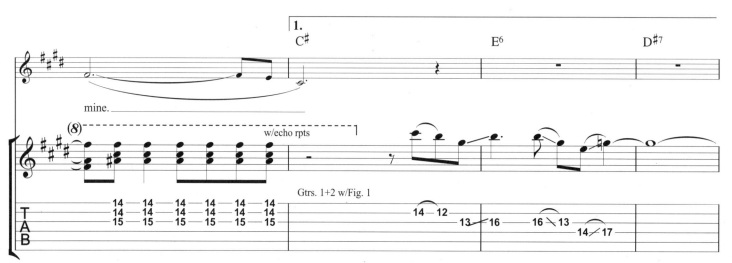

80

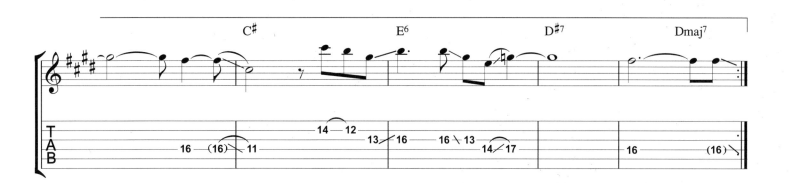

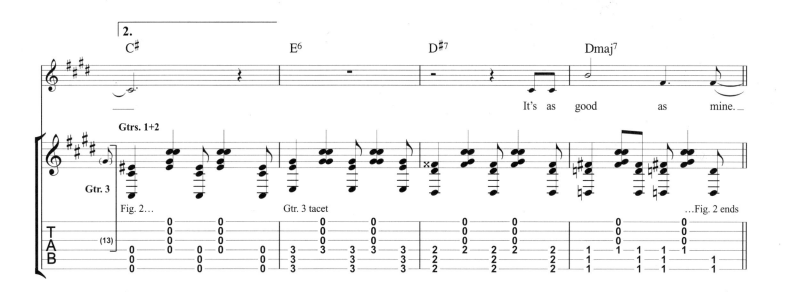

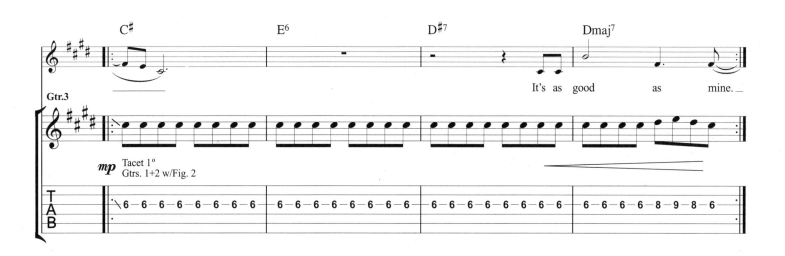

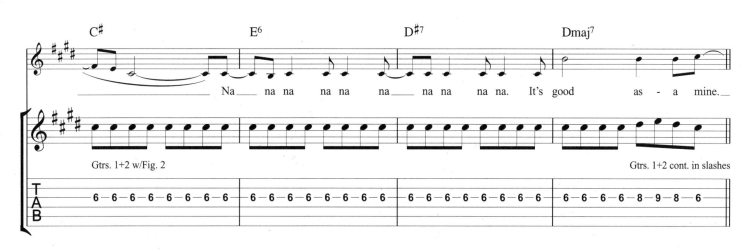

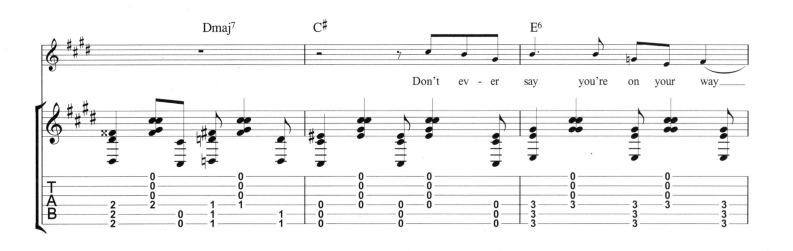

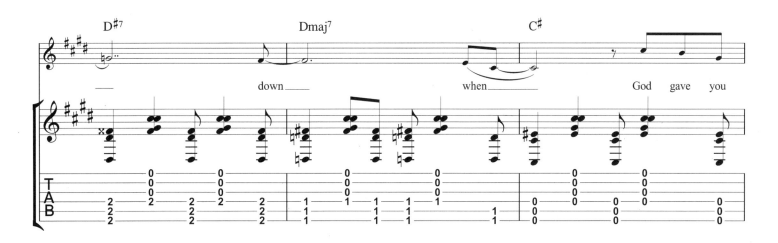

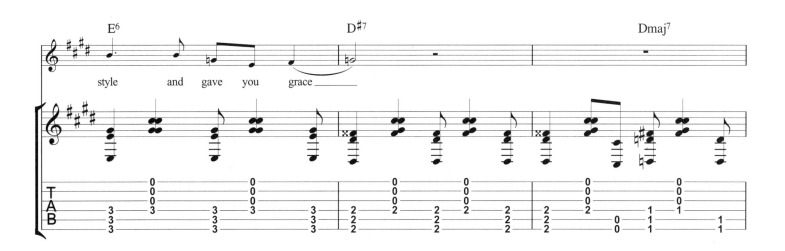

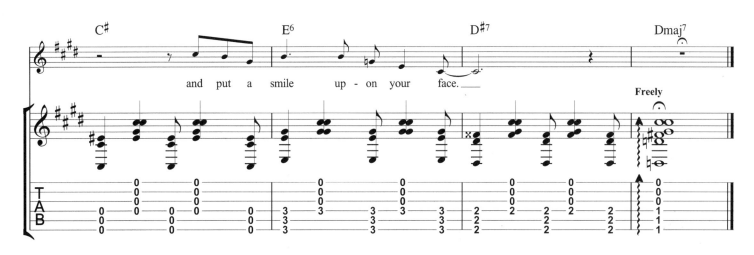

GRAVITY

Words & Music by
Guy Berryman, Jon Buckland, Will Champion & Chris Martin

All gtrs. Capo 3rd fret
Piano chords

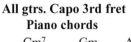
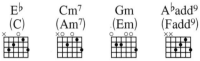

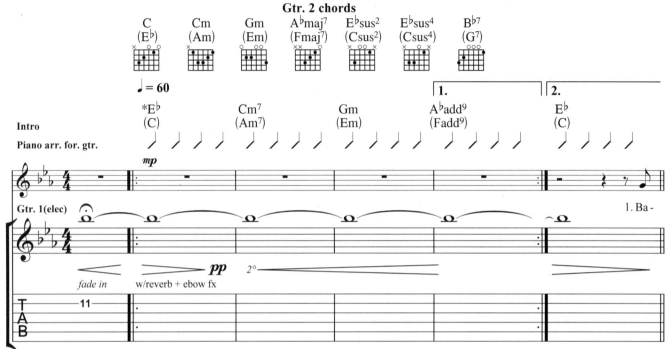

*Symbols in parentheses represent chord names with respect to capoed gtr. (Tab 0 = 2nd fret)
Symbols above represent actual sounding chords.

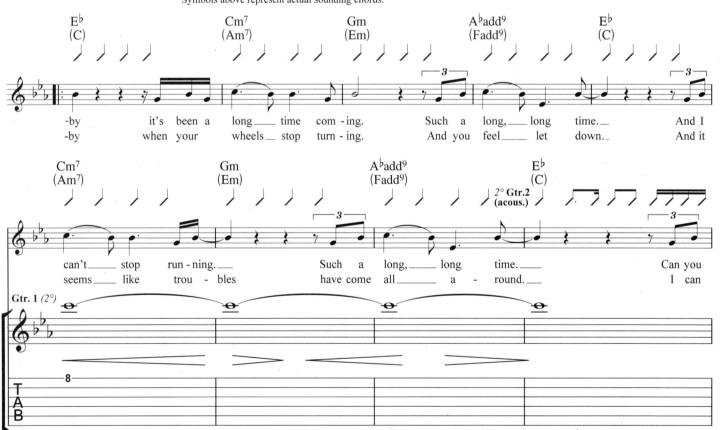

looked up at the sun and I could see oh, the way that gra-vi-ty pulls on you and me.

And then I looked up at the sky and saw the sun and the way

cont. sim. vib.

that gra-vi-ty push-es on ev-'ry-one, on ev-'ry-one.

THE HARDEST PART

Words & Music by
Guy Berryman, Jon Buckland, Will Champion & Chris Martin

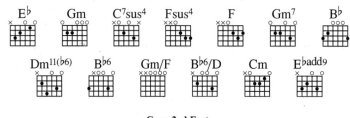

Capo 3rd Fret

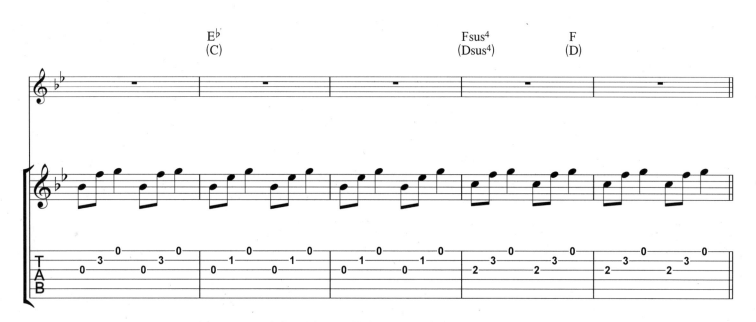

89

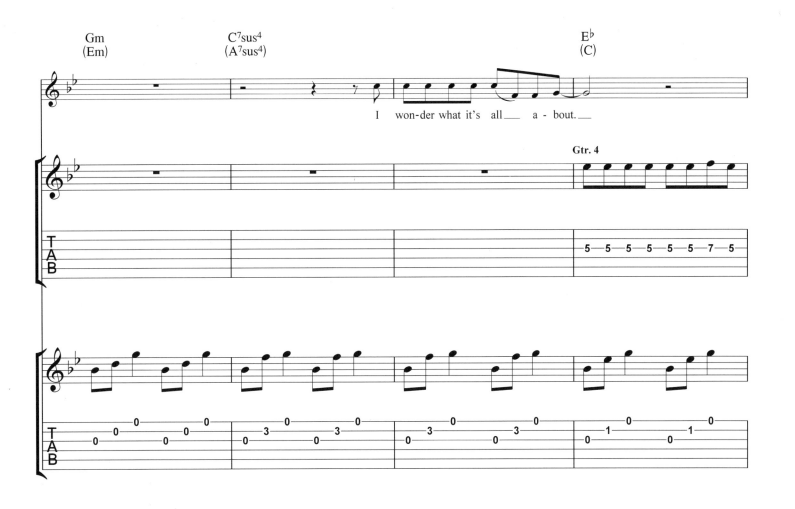

I won-der what it's all___ a - bout.___

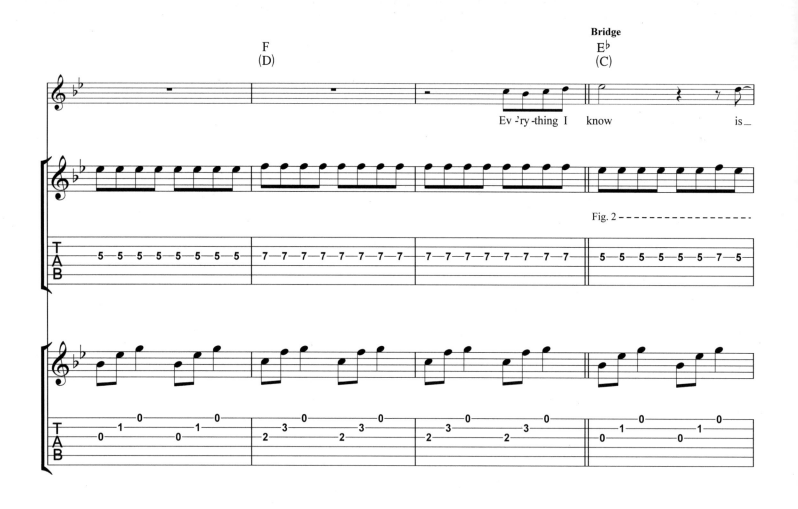

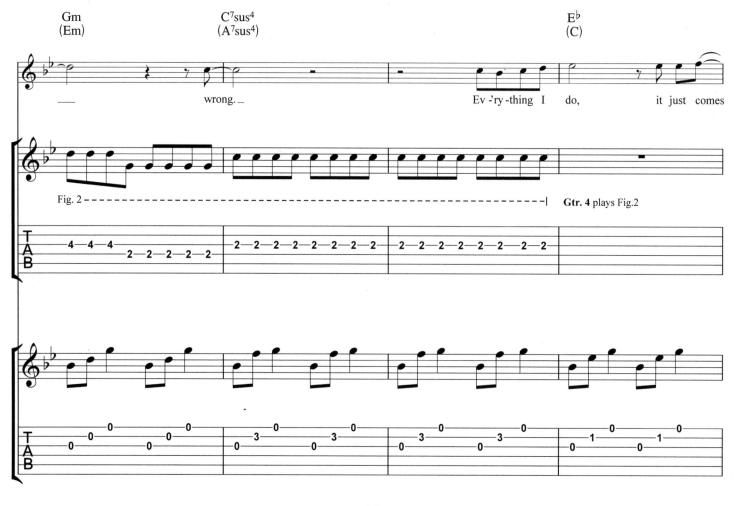

94

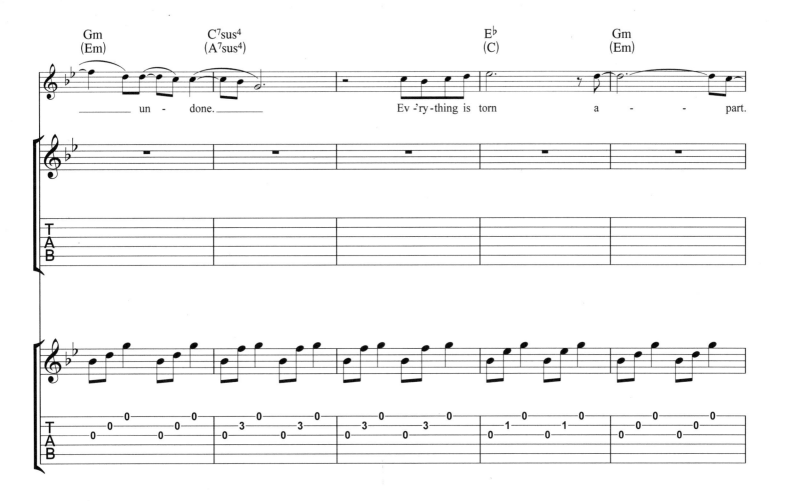

HIGH SPEED

Words & Music by
Guy Berryman, Jon Buckland, Will Champion & Chris Martin

98

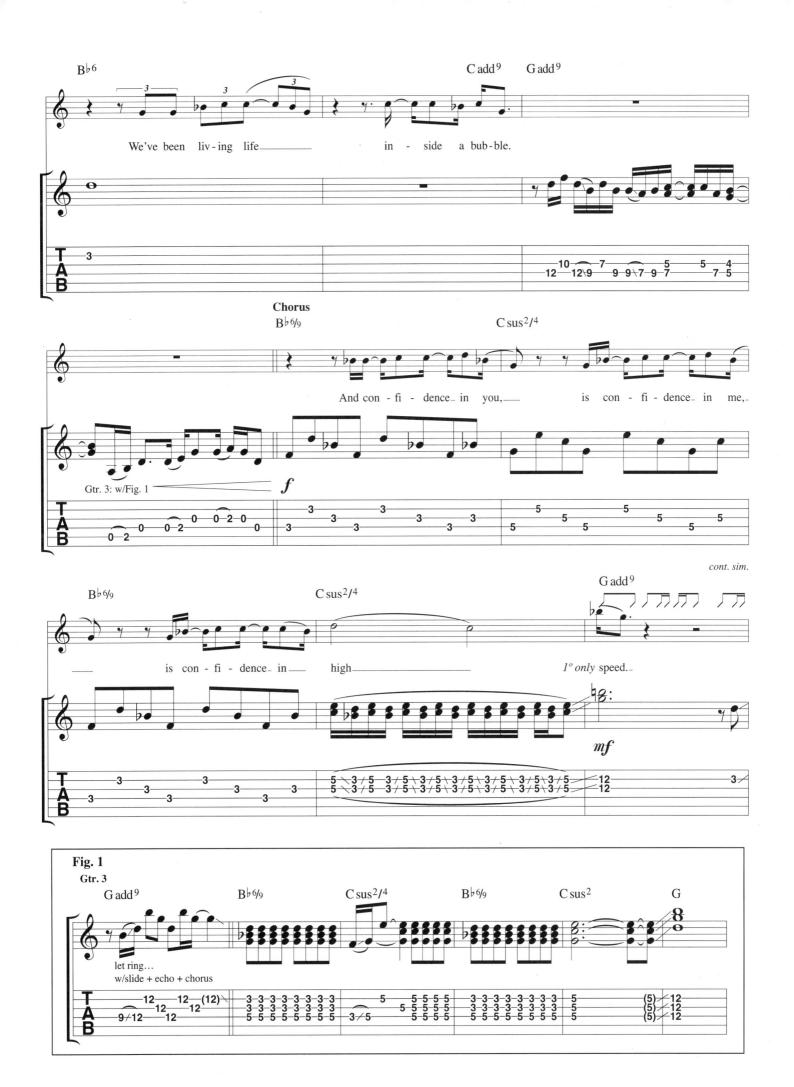

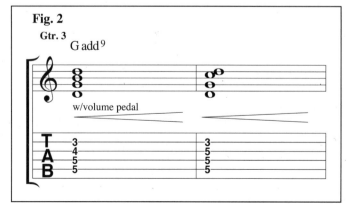

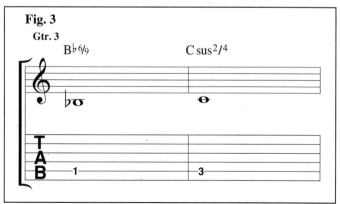

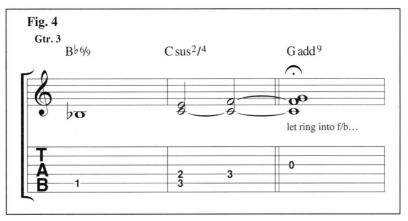

101

HELP IS ROUND THE CORNER

Words & Music by
Guy Berryman, Jon Buckland, Will Champion & Chris Martin

HOW YOU SEE THE WORLD No. 2

Words & Music by
Guy Berryman, Jon Buckland, Will Champion & Chris Martin

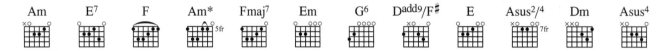

Tune all strings down one semitone

♩ = 66

1. They put the world in a tin can,__ black - mar - ket con - tra - band.__ And it

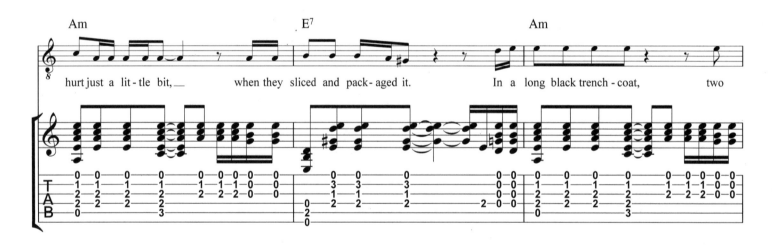

hurt just a lit - tle bit,__ when they sliced and pack - aged it. In a long black trench - coat, two

hands a- round the throat. Oh,__ you wan - na get it right some - times,__ 2. There's so

* Use T on 6

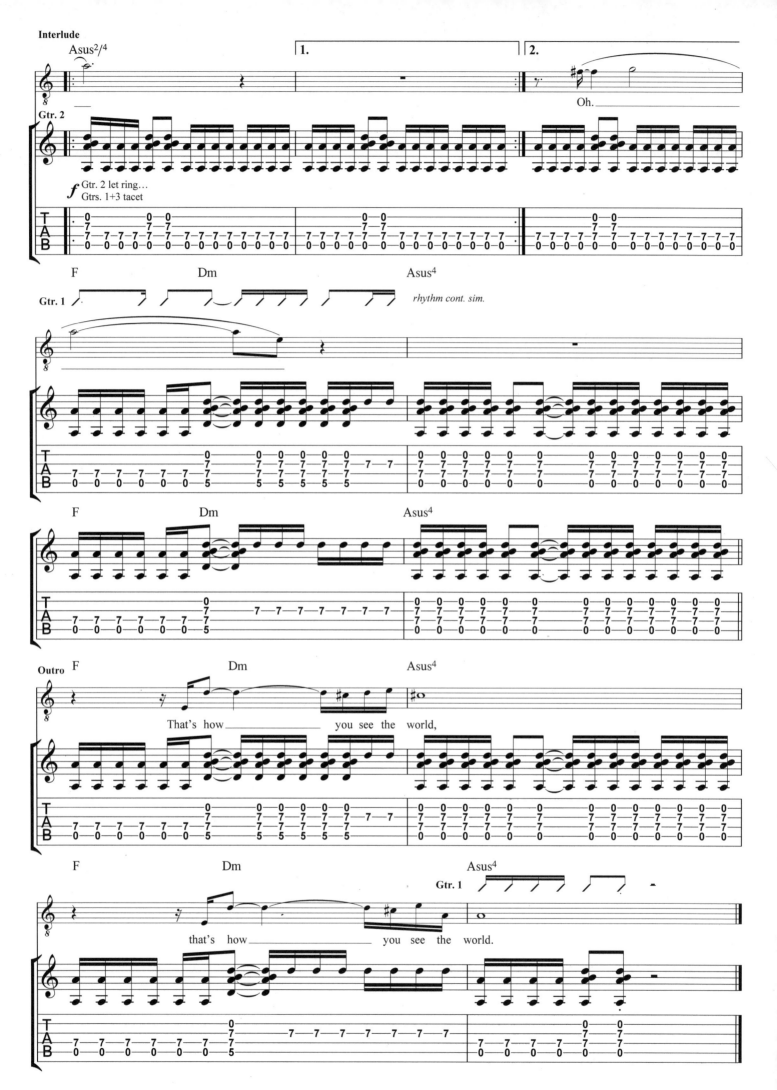

I BLOOM BLAUM

Words & Music by
Guy Berryman, Jon Buckland, Will Champion & Chris Martin

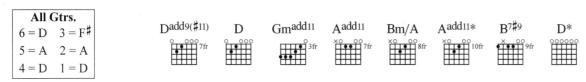

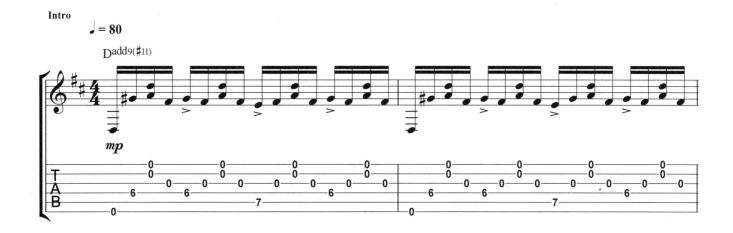

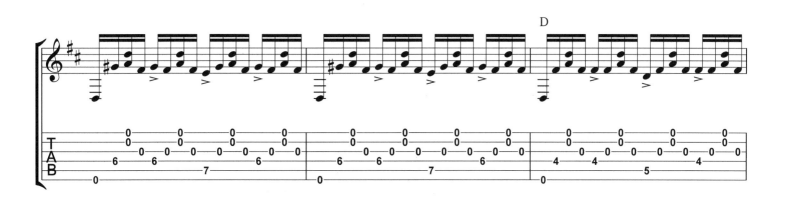

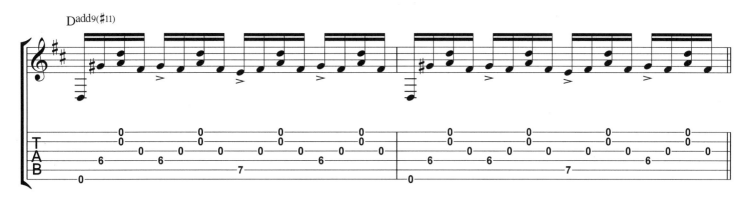

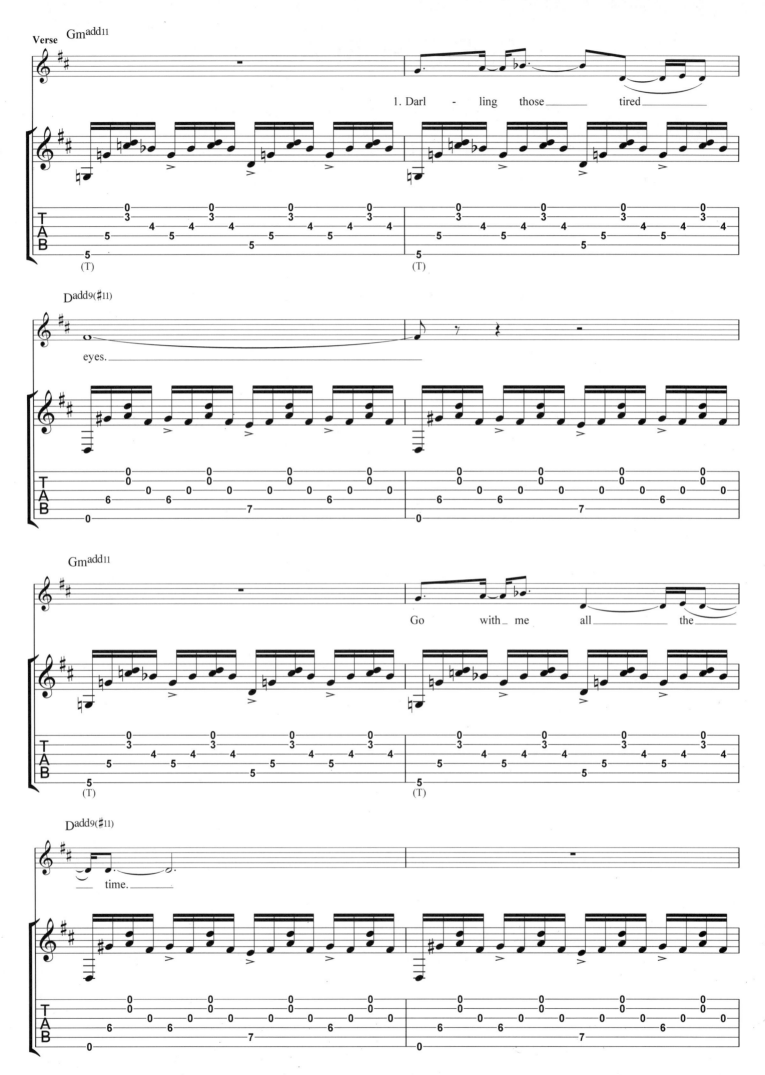

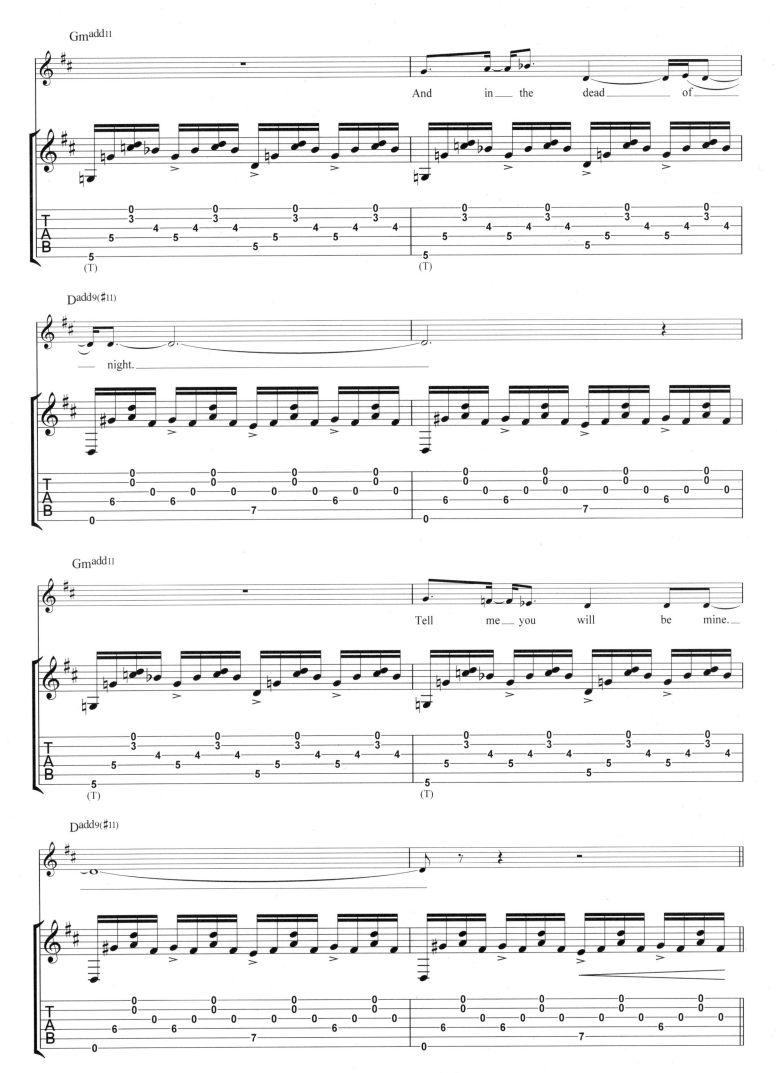

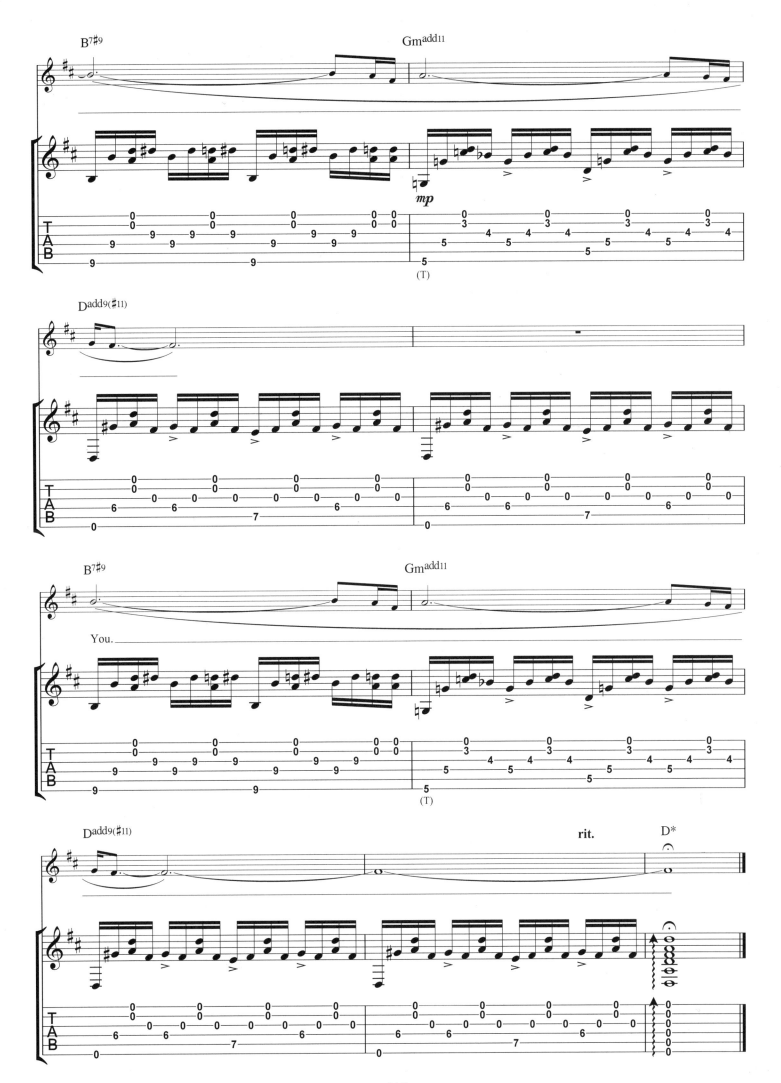

I RAN AWAY

Words & Music by
Guy Berryman, Jon Buckland, Will Champion & Chris Martin

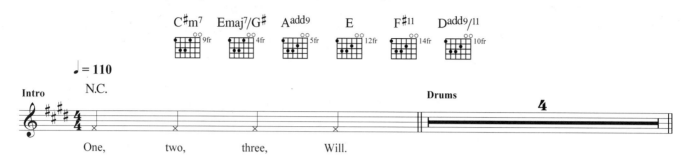

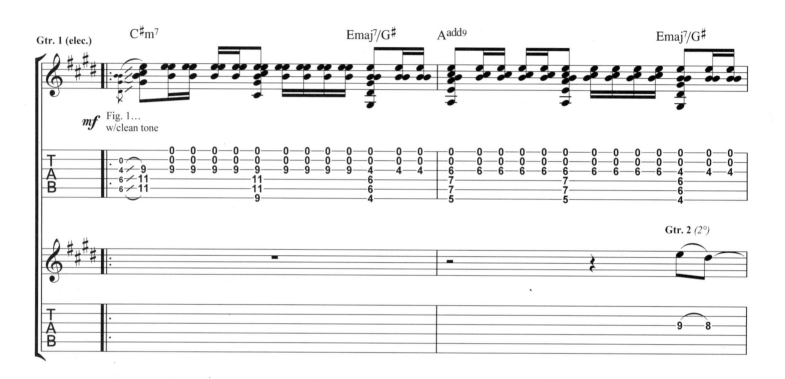

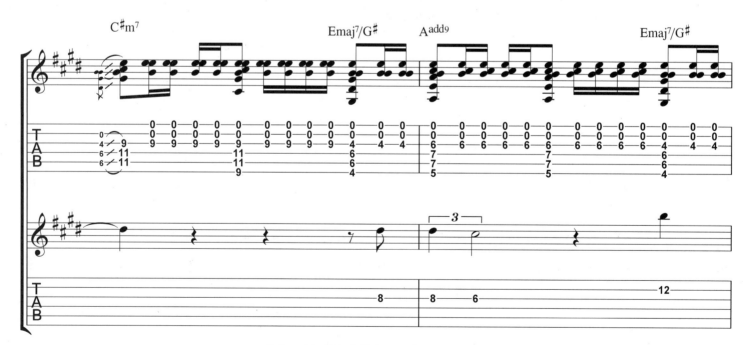

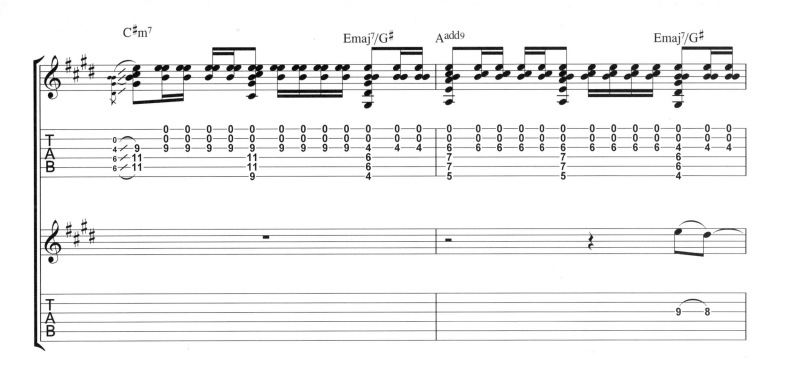

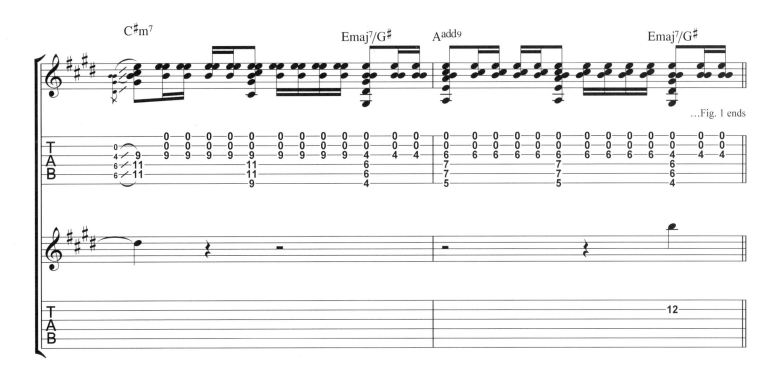

...Fig. 1 ends

Gtr. 1 w/Fig. 1 (x2)

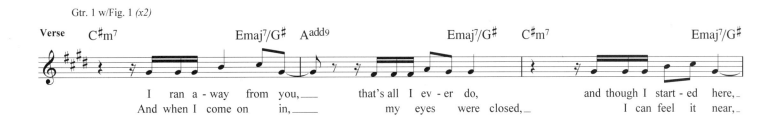

Verse

I ran a-way from you,___ that's all I ev-er do, and though I start-ed here,___
And when I come on in,___ my eyes were closed,_ I can feel it near,_

_____ I ran a-way from you.___ I'm gon-na come on in _____ and see it through,_
sun's so close,_ When I come on out _____ in my own

117

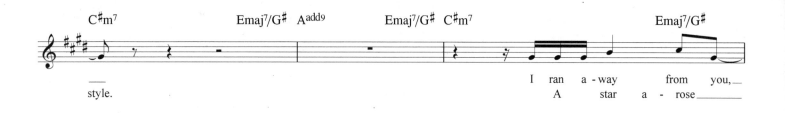

C#m⁷   Emaj⁷/G#   Aadd9   Emaj⁷/G#   C#m⁷   Emaj⁷/G#

— I ran a - way from you,
style.

Aadd9   Emaj⁷/G#   C#m⁷   Emaj⁷/G#

— that's all I ev - er do._____ And when I heard your call—
— in my own cage,_____ I'm stuck in life—

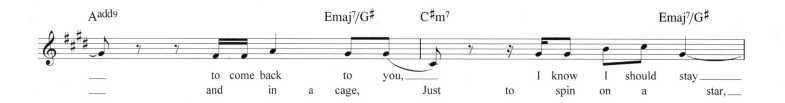

Aadd9   Emaj⁷/G#   C#m⁷   Emaj⁷/G#

— to come back to you,_____ I know I should stay_____
— and in a cage, Just to spin on a star,—

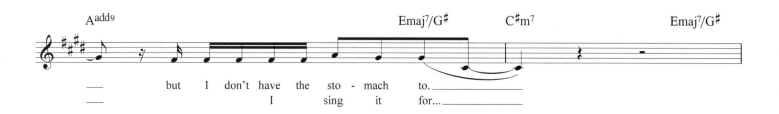

Aadd9   Emaj⁷/G#   C#m⁷   Emaj⁷/G#

— but I don't have the sto - mach to._____
— I sing it for..._____

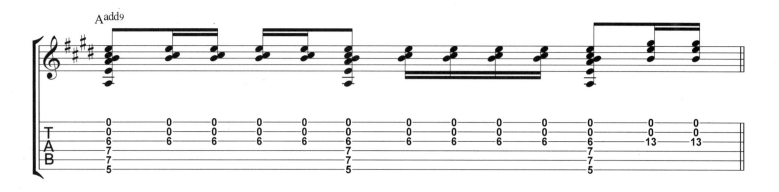

Aadd9

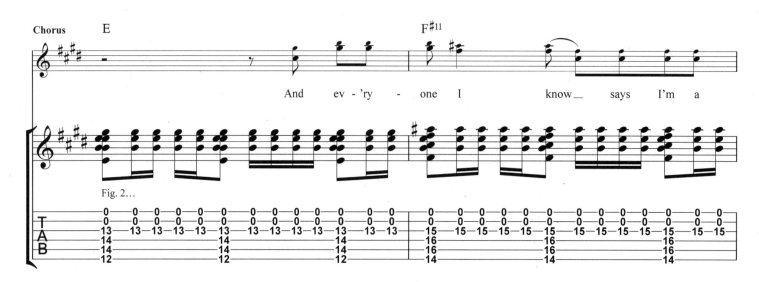

Chorus   E   F#11

And ev - 'ry - one I know— says I'm a

Fig. 2…

118

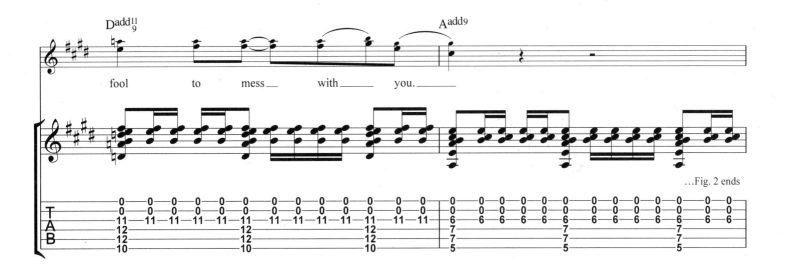

fool to mess with you.

...Fig. 2 ends

And ev-'ry-one I know says it's a stu-pid thing to do.

I have your love on call and yet my

Day is not so full. And I did

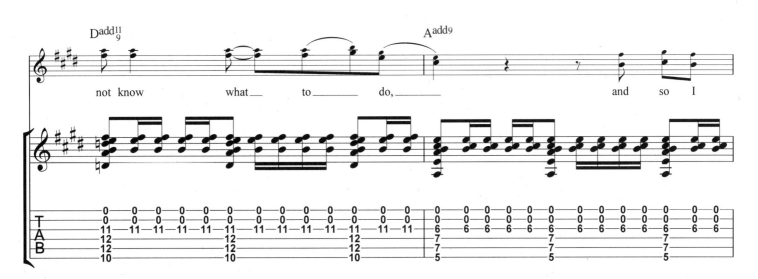

not know what to do, and so I

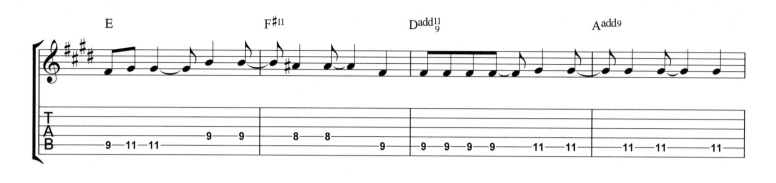

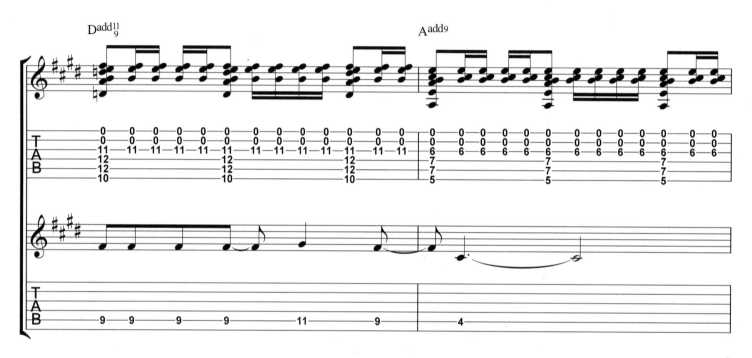

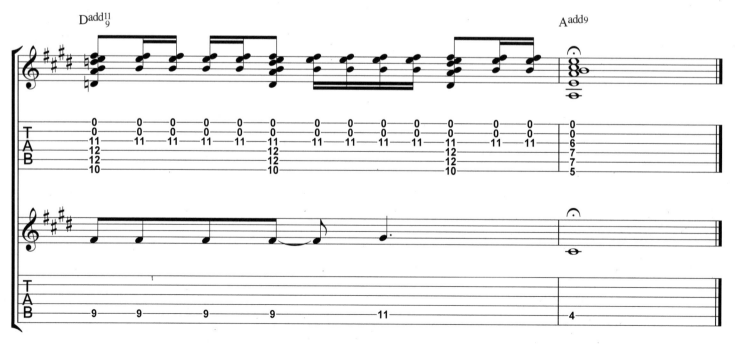

ONLY SUPERSTITION

Words & Music by
Guy Berryman, Jon Buckland, Will Champion & Chris Martin

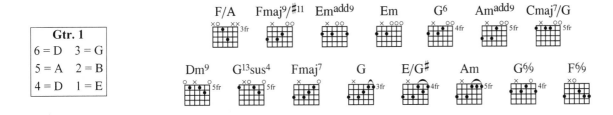

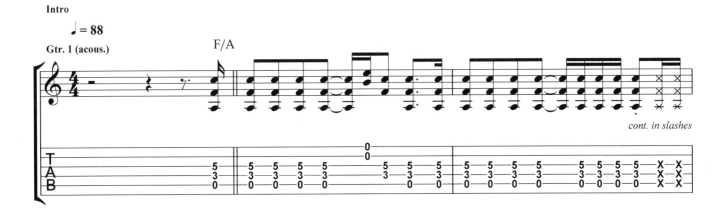

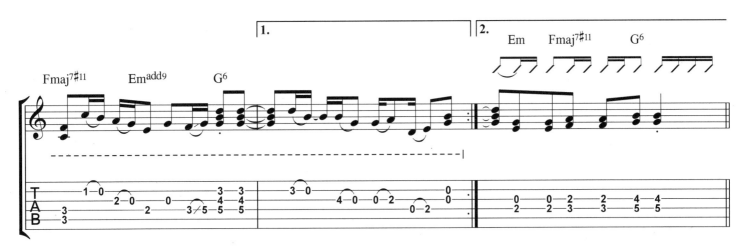

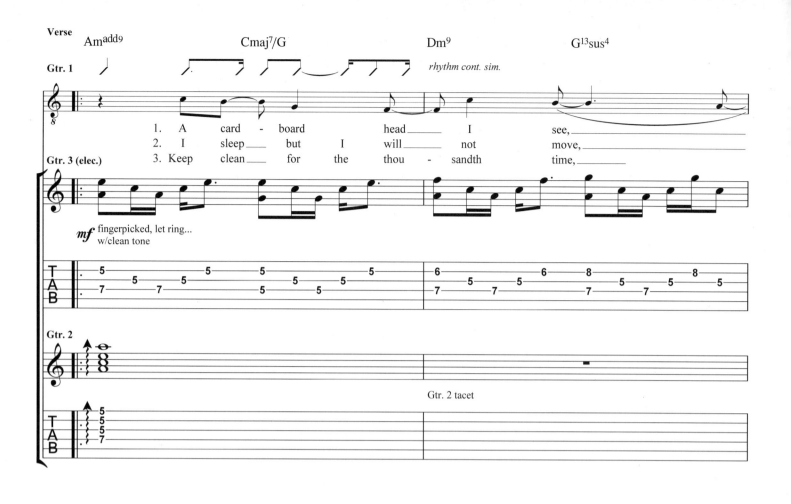

1. A card - board head_____ I see,_____
2. I sleep_____ but I will_____ not move,_____
3. Keep clean_____ for the thou - sandth time,_____

mf fingerpicked, let ring...
w/clean tone

Gtr. 2 tacet

___ has found_____ its way_____ to me.
___ I'm too scared to leave_____ my room.
stand still and wait_____ in line._____

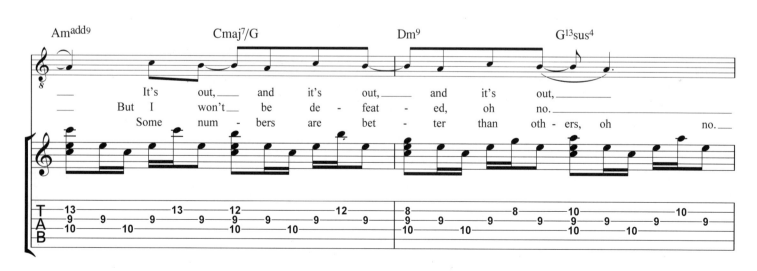

___ It's out,_____ and it's out,_____ and it's out,_____
___ But I won't_____ be de - feat - ed, oh no._____
Some num - bers are bet - ter than oth - ers, oh no._____

IN MY PLACE

Words & Music by
Guy Berryman, Jon Buckland, Will Champion & Chris Martin

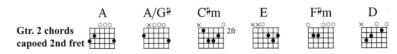

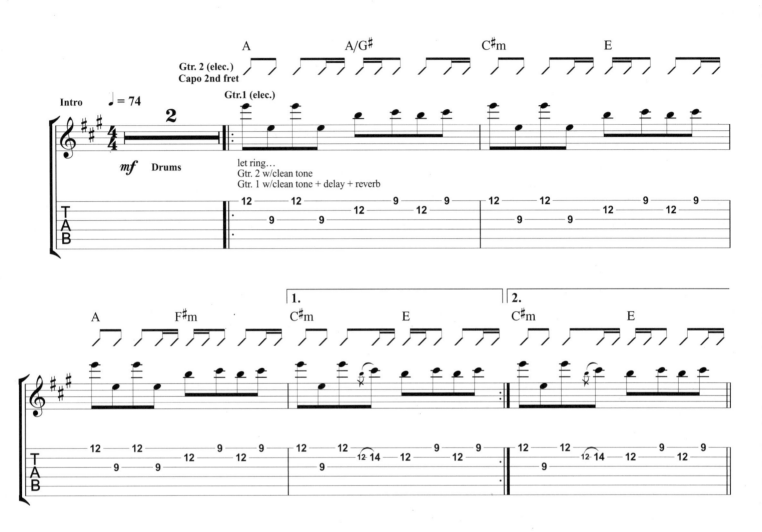

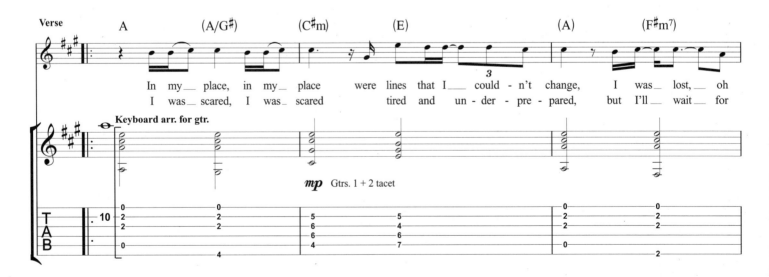

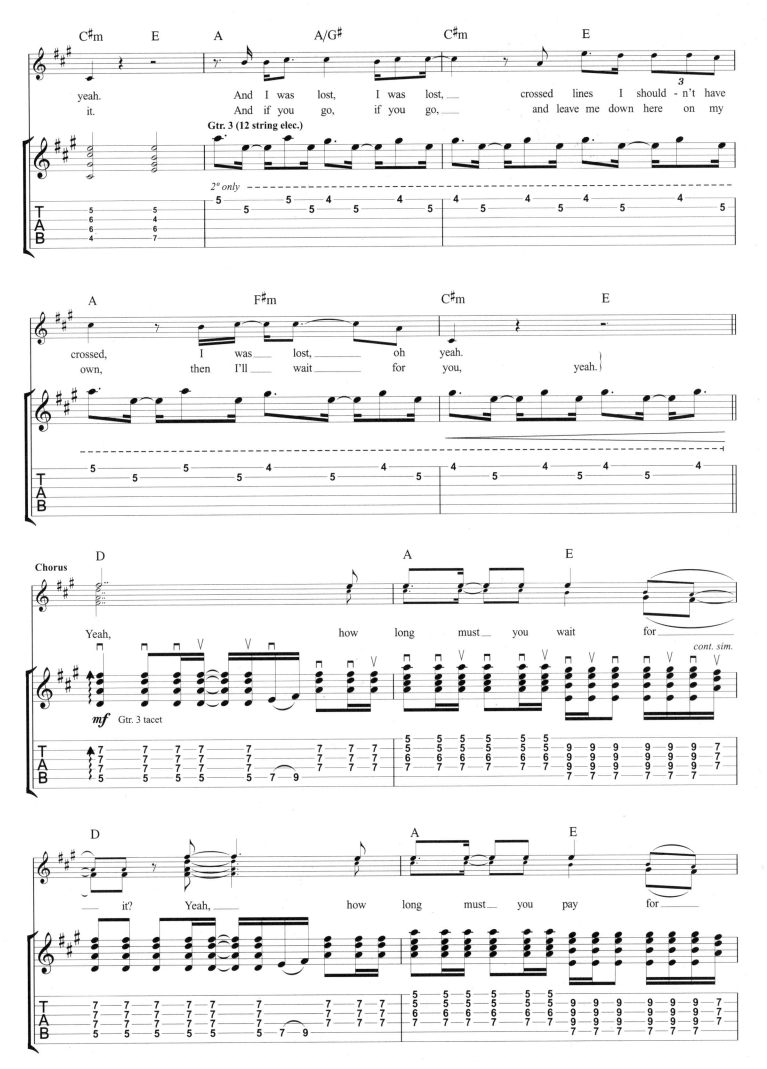

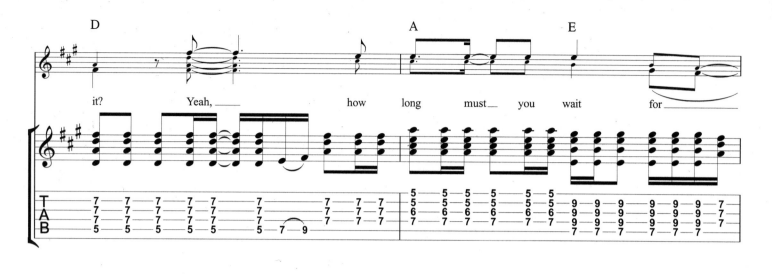

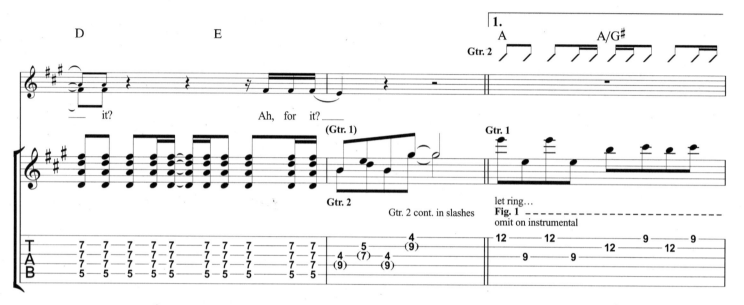

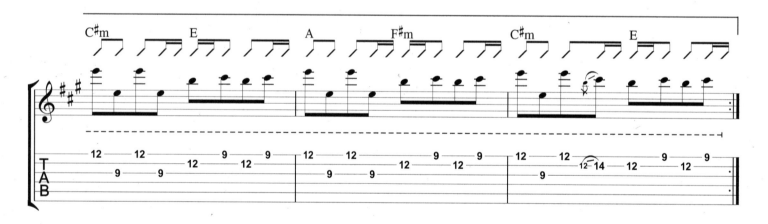

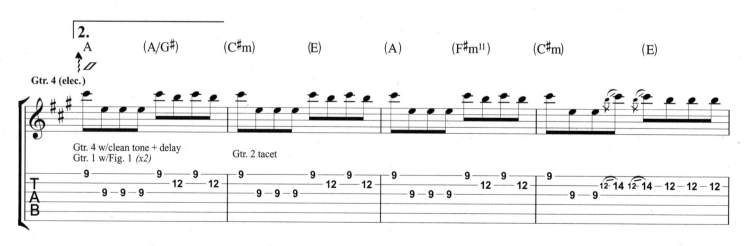

MURDER

Words & Music by
Guy Berryman, Jon Buckland, Will Champion & Chris Martin

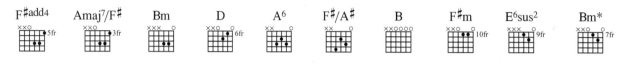

All Gtrs Capo 4th fret

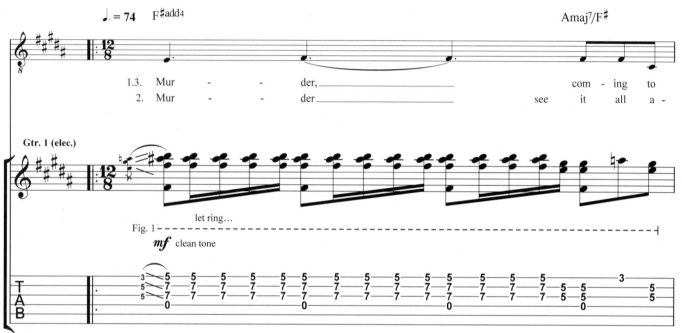

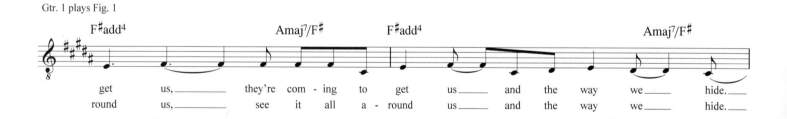

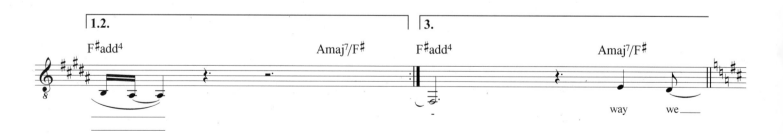

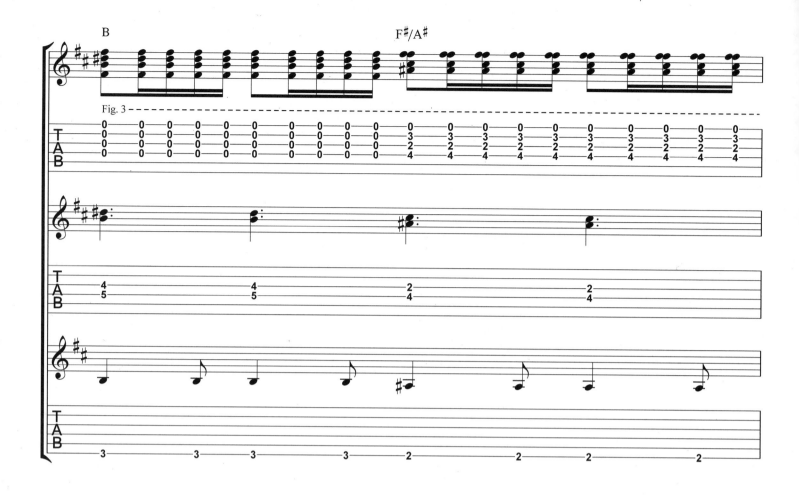

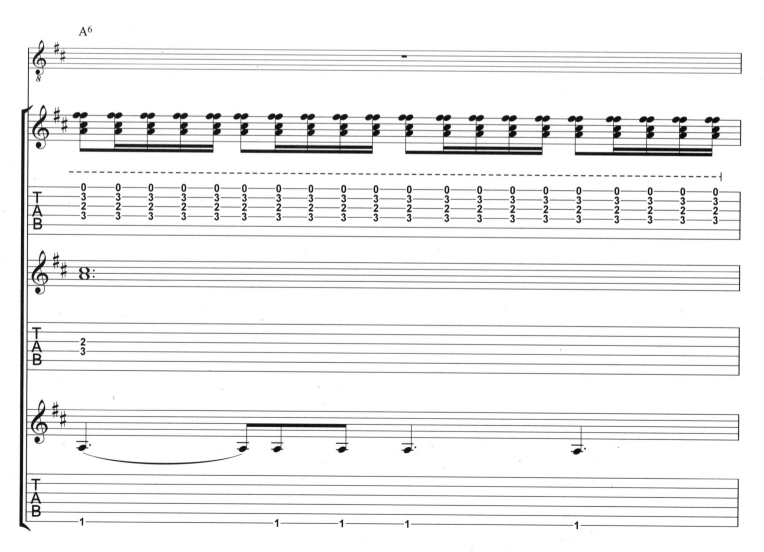

Verse

1. Tie me to a tree, ___ tie my hands a-bove my ___ head. ___
2. Come (and) spit at us, ___ come and throw your weight a-round. ___

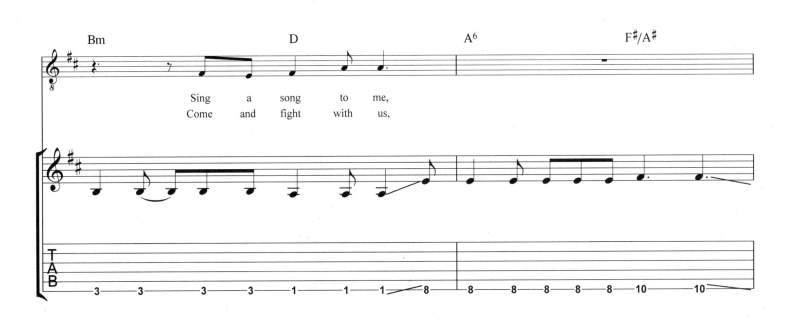

Sing a song to me,
Come and fight with us,

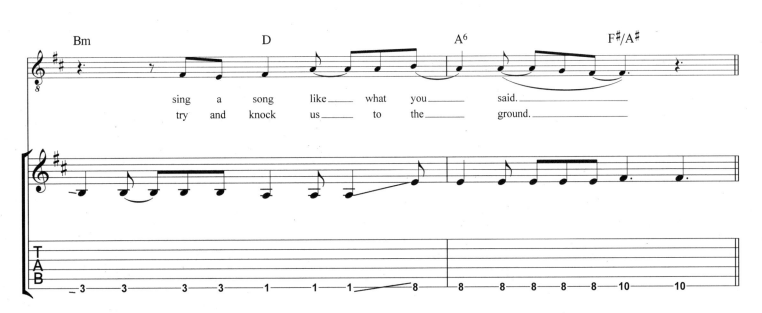

sing a song like ___ what you ___ said. ___
try and knock us ___ to the ___ ground. ___

Gtr. 1 w/ Fig. 3

Gtr. 1 w/ Fig. 1

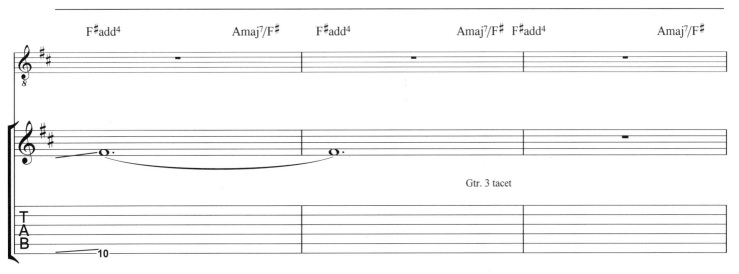

Gtr. 3 tacet

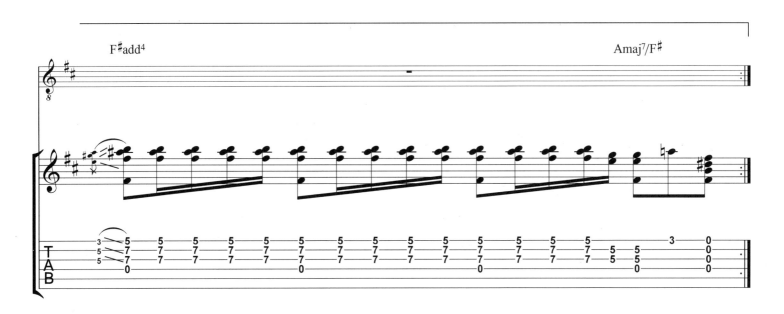

137

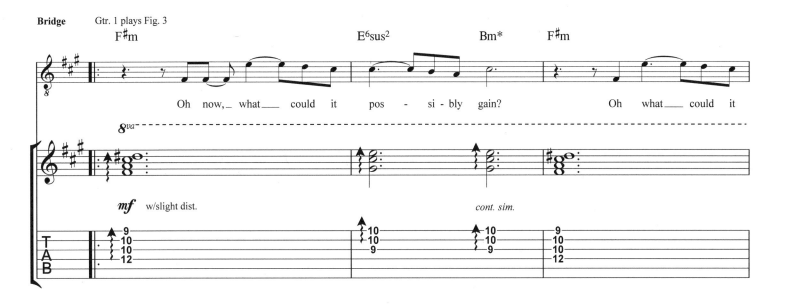

Bridge Gtr. 1 plays Fig. 3

Oh now,__ what__ could it pos - si - bly gain? Oh what__ could it

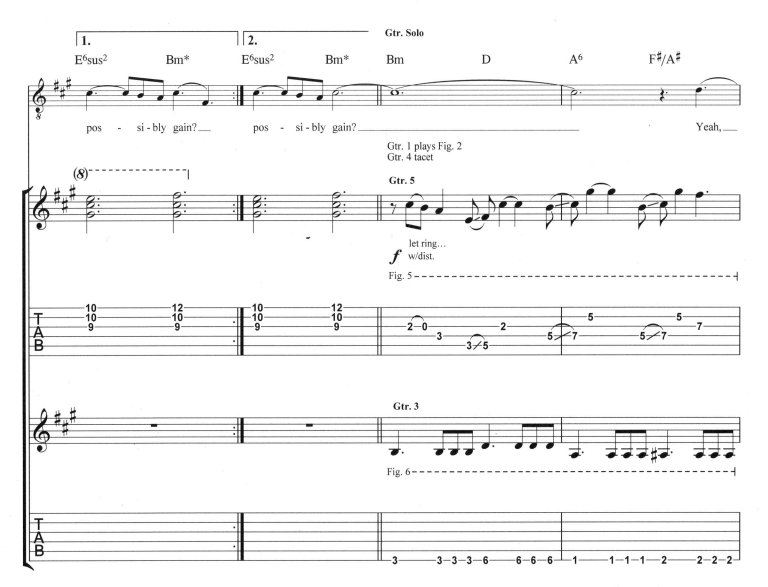

1. **2.** **Gtr. Solo**

pos - si - bly gain?__ pos - si - bly gain?__ Yeah,__

Gtr. 1 plays Fig. 2
Gtr. 4 tacet

Gtr. 5 plays Fig. 5
Gtr. 3 plays Fig. 6
Bm
D
A6
F♯/A♯
and I cry mur -
Bm
D
A6
F♯/A♯
- der, mur - - der.
I cry
Gtr. 1 plays Fig. 3
B
F♯/A♯
A6
mur - - - - - der,
TAB
Gtr. 3
TAB
TAB
TAB

NO MORE KEEPING MY FEET ON THE GROUND

Words & Music by
Guy Berryman, Jon Buckland, Will Champion & Chris Martin

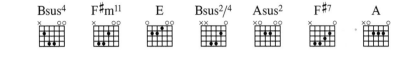

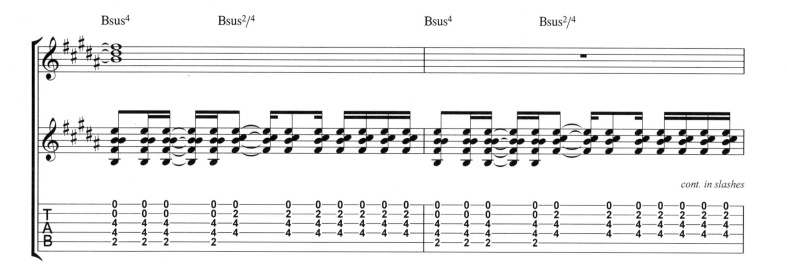

cont. in slashes

Gtr. 1 plays Fig. 1

Verse

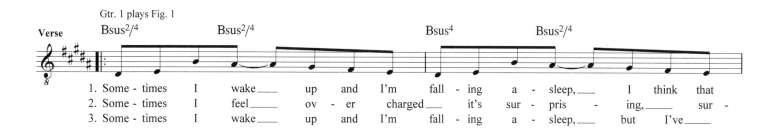

1. Some - times I wake____ up and I'm fall - ing a - sleep,____ I think that
2. Some - times I feel____ ov - er charged____ it's sur - pris - ing,____ sur -
3. Some - times I wake____ up and I'm fall - ing a - sleep,____ but I've____

may - be the cur - tains are clos - ing on me.____ But I wake____
-pris - ing - ly good,____ to be mov - ing a - round. So I wake____
got to get go - ing, so much that I want - ed to do,____

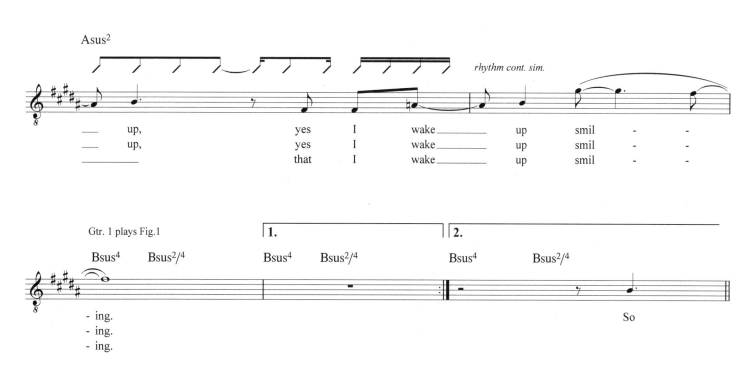

rhythm cont. sim.

____ up, yes I wake_____ up smil - -
____ up, yes I wake_____ up smil - -
_____ that I wake_____ up smil - -

Gtr. 1 plays Fig.1

1.   **2.**

- ing.
- ing.
- ing.   So

143

Verse

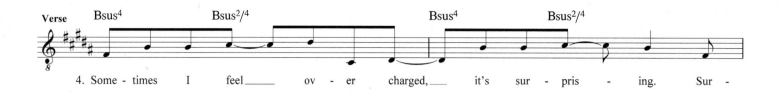

4. Some - times I feel____ ov - er charged,____ it's sur - pris - ing. Sur -

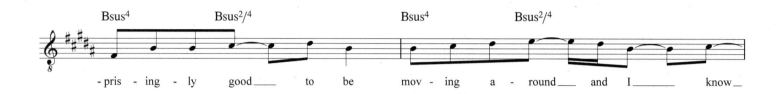

-pris - ing - ly good____ to be mov - ing a - round____ and I____ know____

Gtr. 1 plays Fig. 1

____ I'll wake up smil - ing._____ So

Pre-chorus

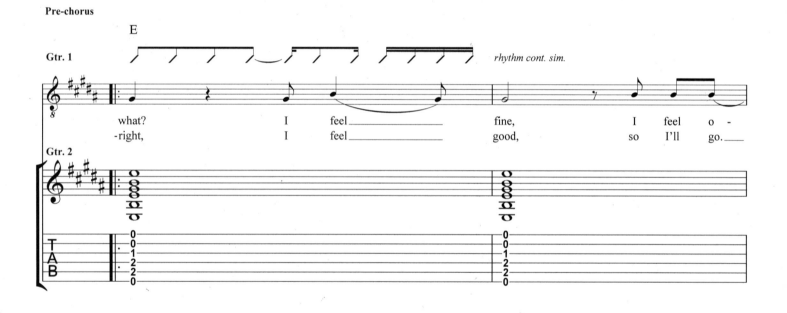

what? I feel_____ fine, I feel o -
-right, I feel_____ good, so I'll go.____

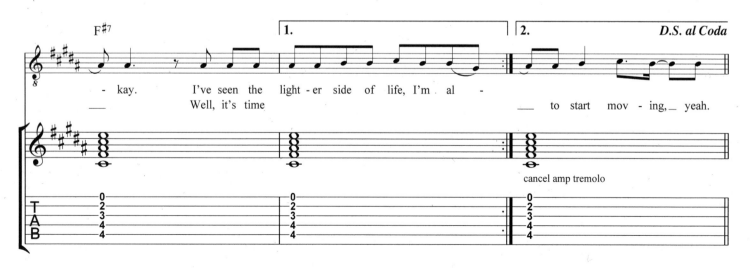

- kay. I've seen the light - er side of life, I'm al -
Well, it's time ____ to start mov - ing,__ yeah.

cancel amp tremolo

147

ONE I LOVE

Words & Music by
Guy Berryman, Jon Buckland, Will Champion & Chris Martin

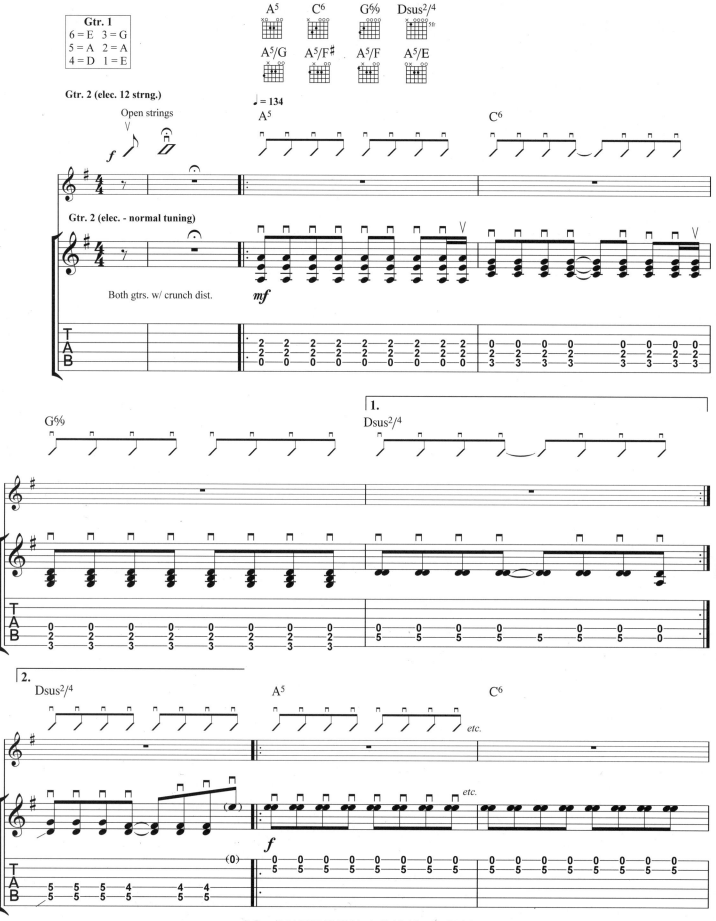

('Cause) your the one I love.

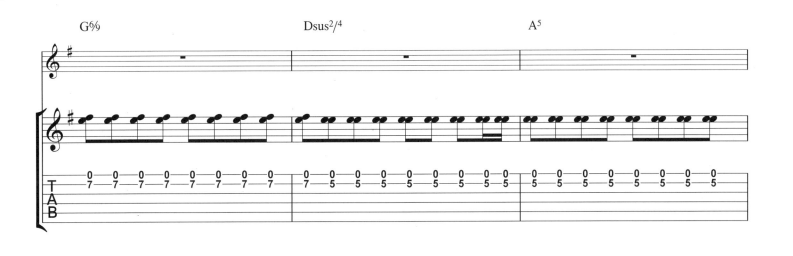

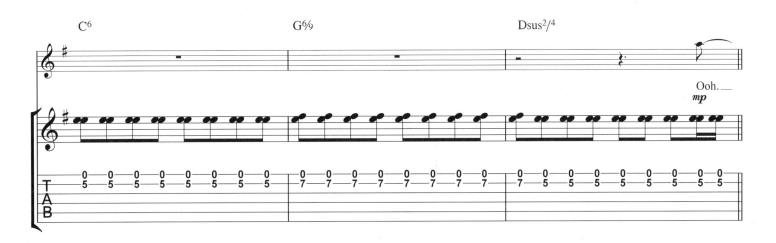

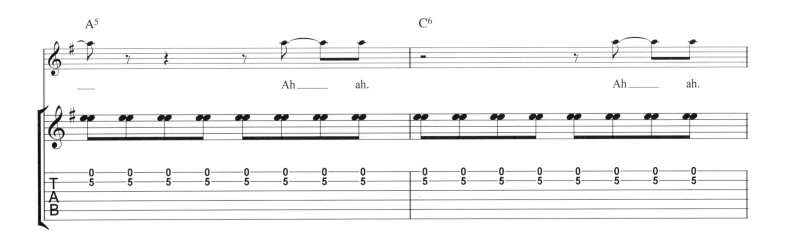

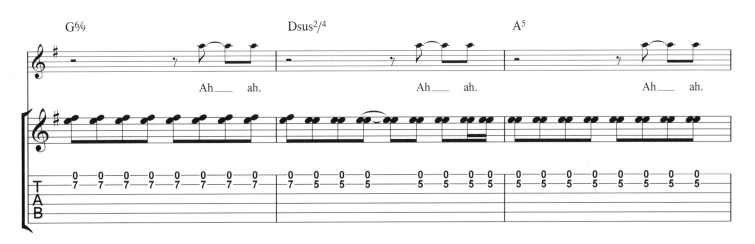

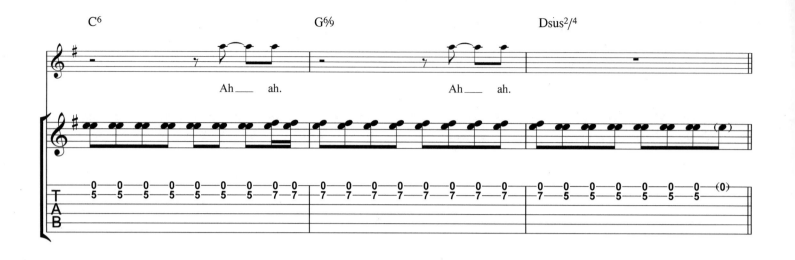

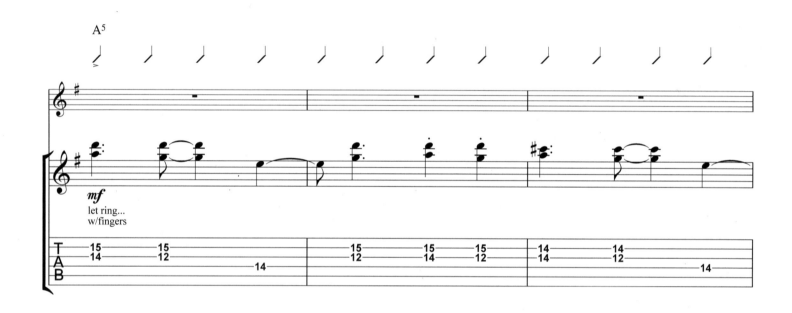

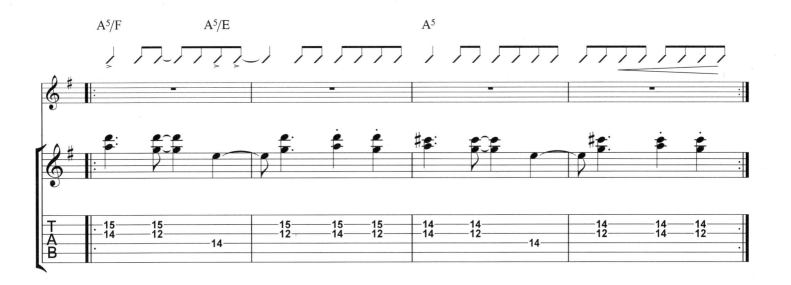

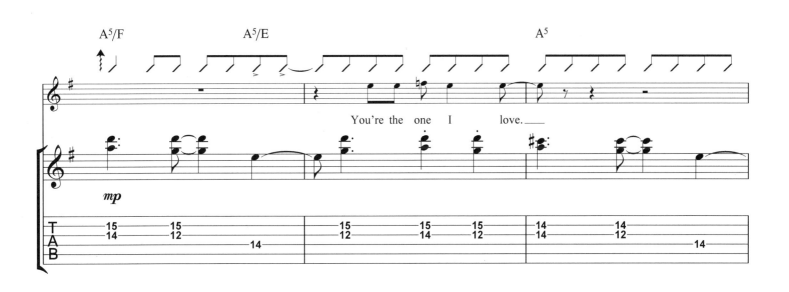

155

POUR ME

Words & Music by
Guy Berryman, Jon Buckland, Will Champion & Chris Martin

157

PROOF

Words & Music by
Guy Berryman, Jon Buckland, Will Champion & Chris Martin

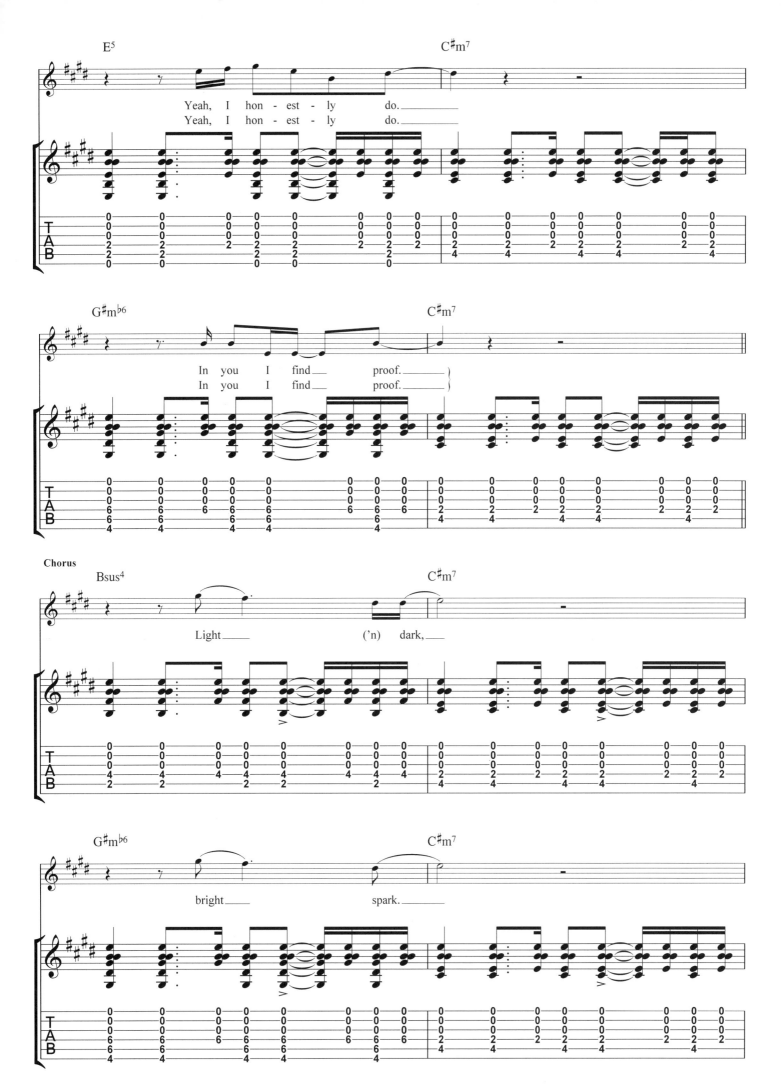

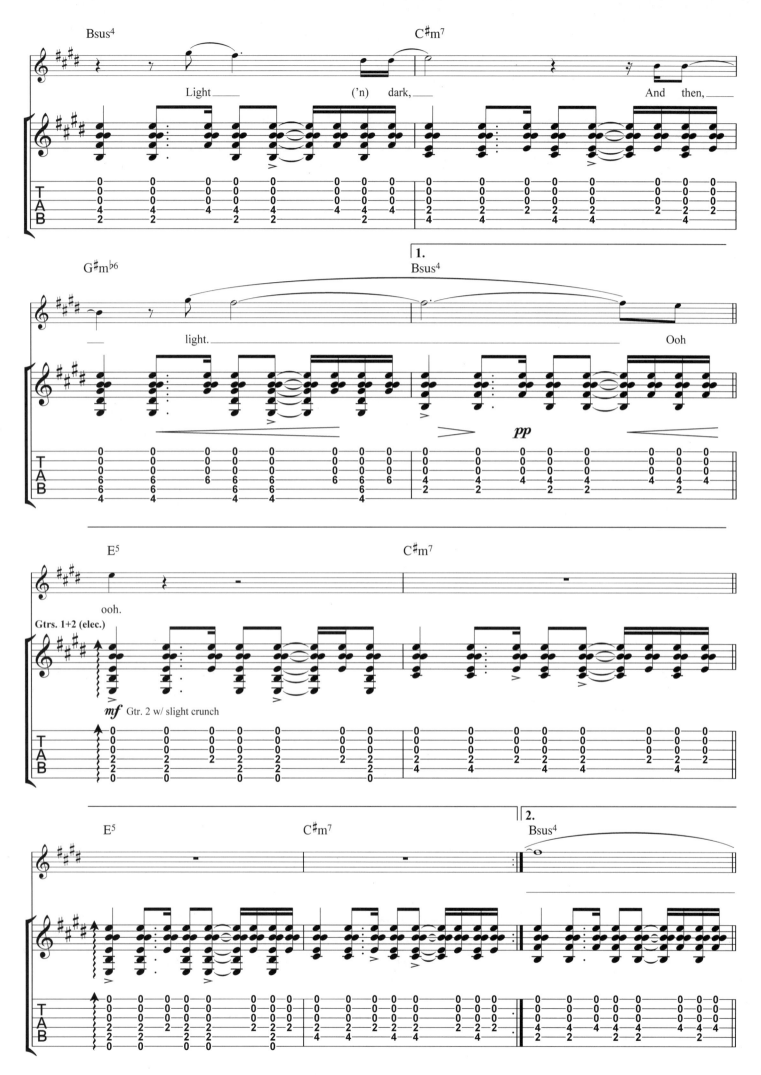

Outro

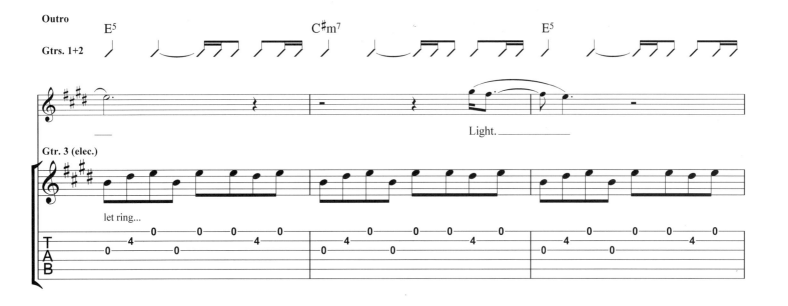

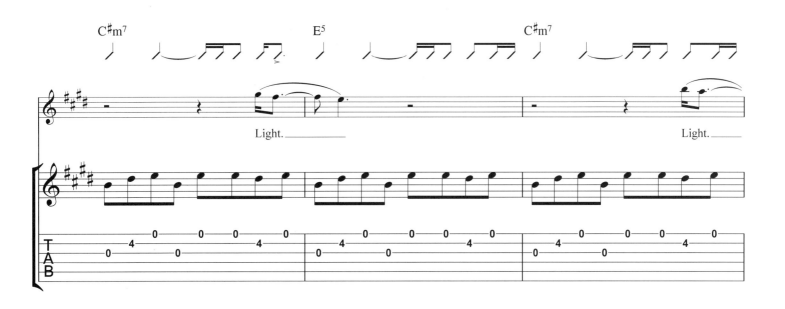

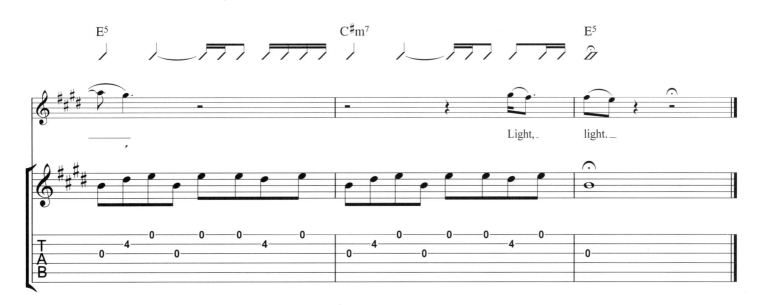

THE SCIENTIST

Words & Music by
Guy Berryman, Jon Buckland, Will Champion & Chris Martin

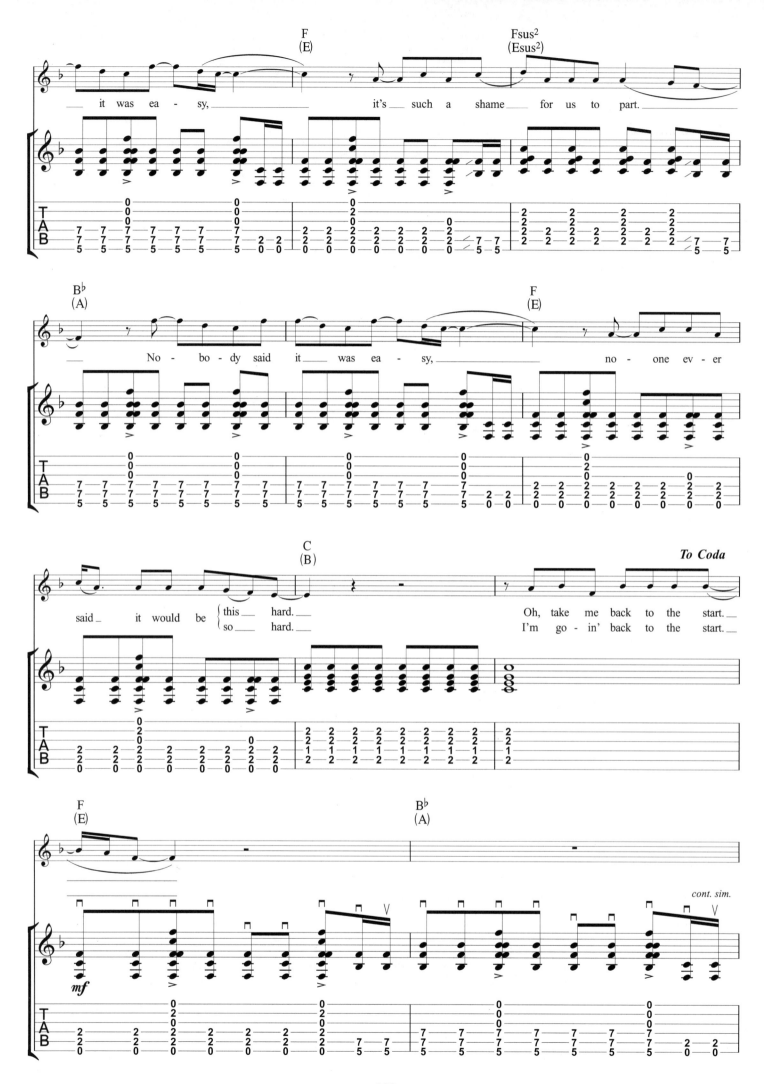

169

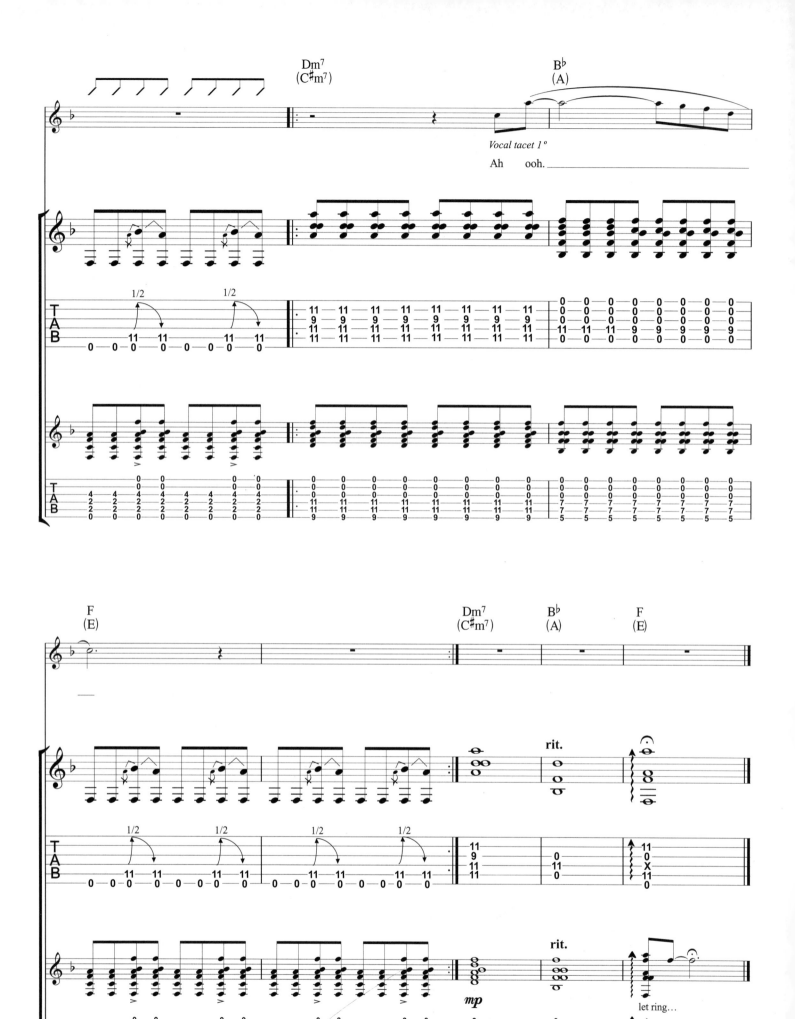

Vocal tacet 1°

Ah   ooh. _____

170

SHIVER

Words & Music by
Guy Berryman, Jon Buckland, Will Champion & Chris Martin

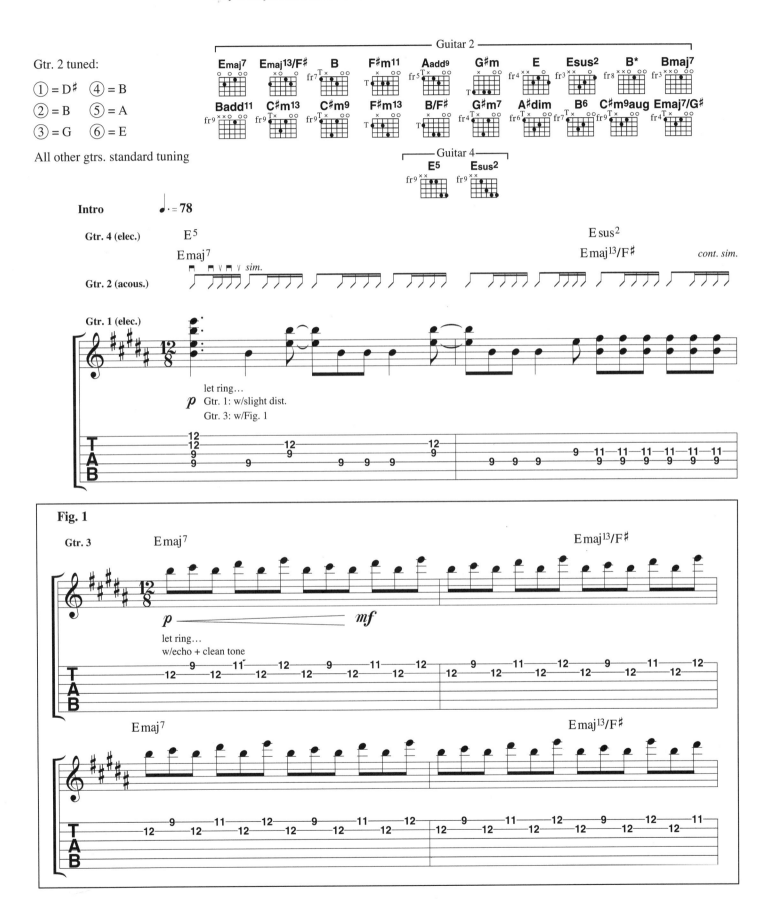

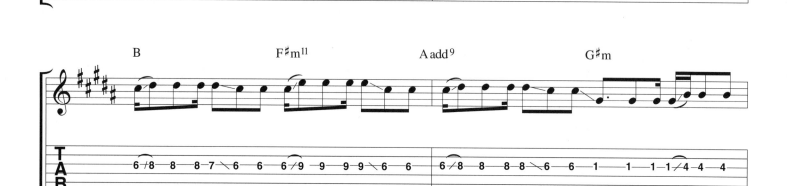

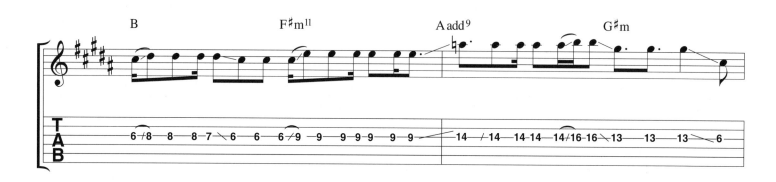

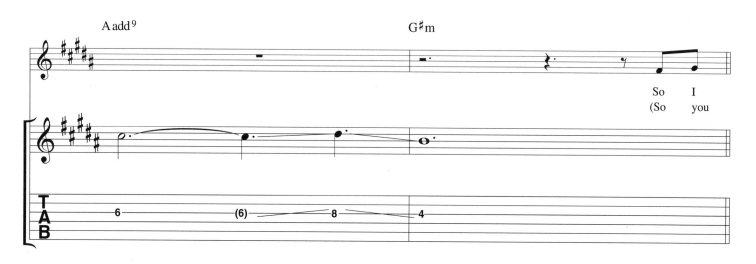

So   I
(So   you

172

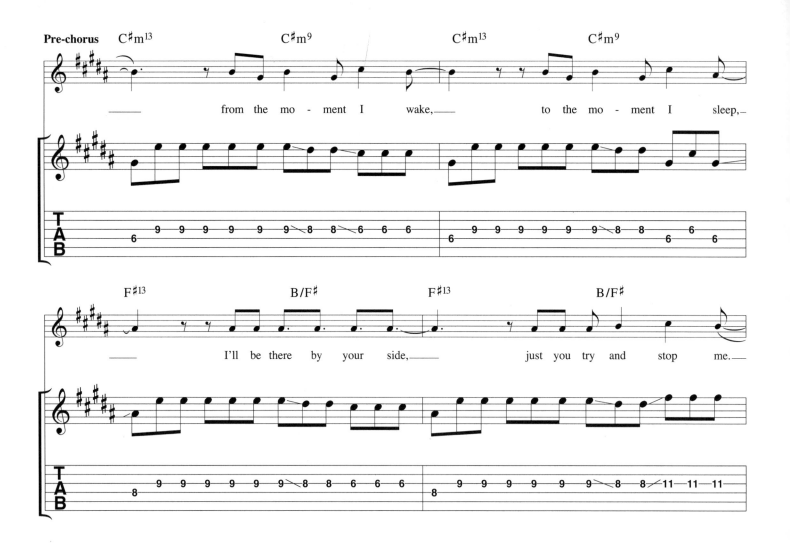

Pre-chorus

from the mo - ment I wake,___ to the mo - ment I sleep,___

I'll be there by your side,___ just you try and stop me.___

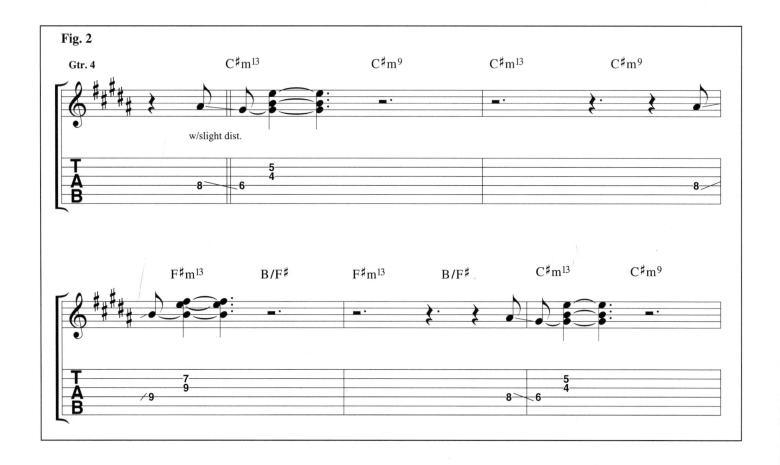

Fig. 2

Gtr. 4

w/slight dist.

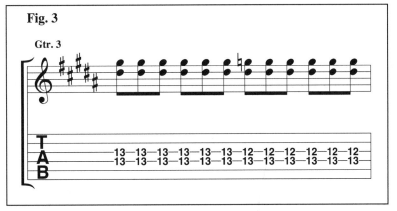

175

and I want you to know_____ that you'll al - ways_____ get your

2° Gtr. 3: w/Fig. 4

way.   I want-ed to_____ say,_____ don't you shi - ver,_____

Chorus

shi - ver,_____

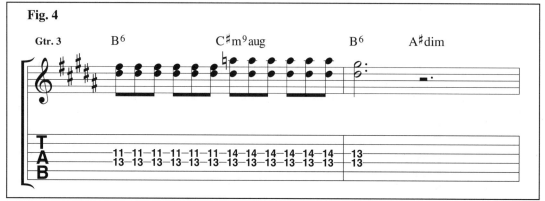

Fig. 4

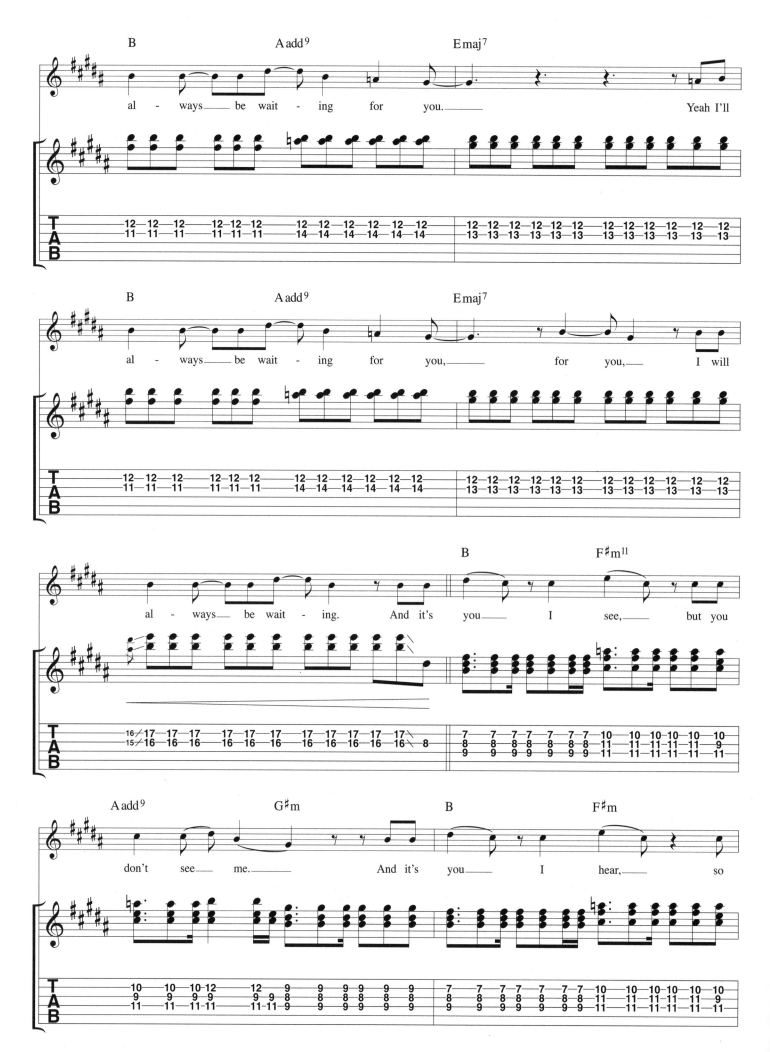

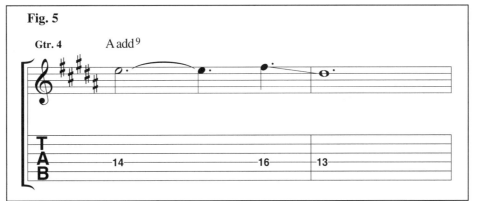

SEE YOU SOON

Words & Music by
Guy Berryman, Jon Buckland, Will Champion & Chris Martin

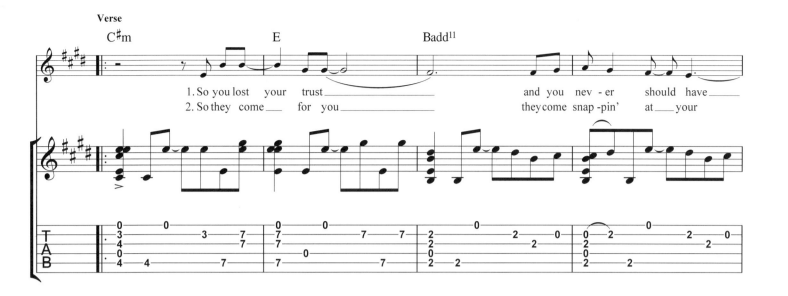

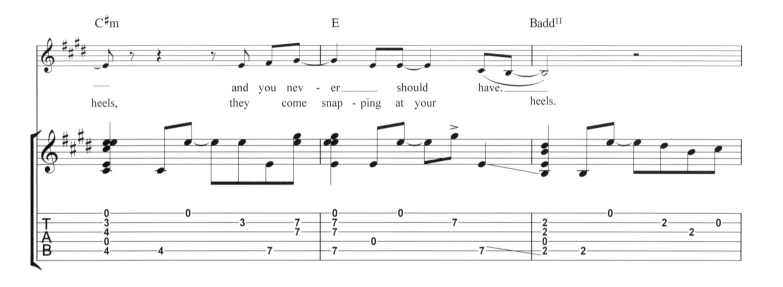

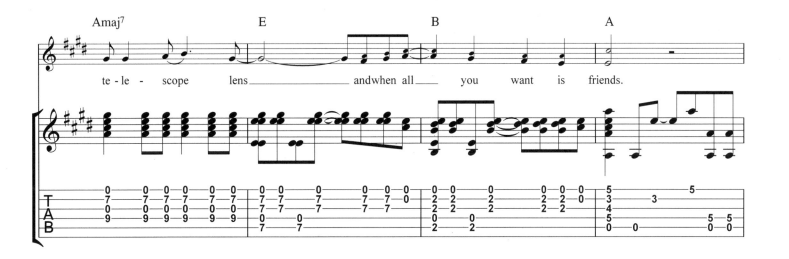

te - le - scope lens_____ andwhen all____ you want is friends.

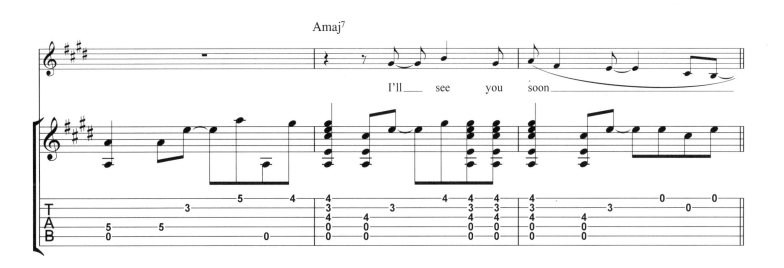

I'll____ see you soon_____

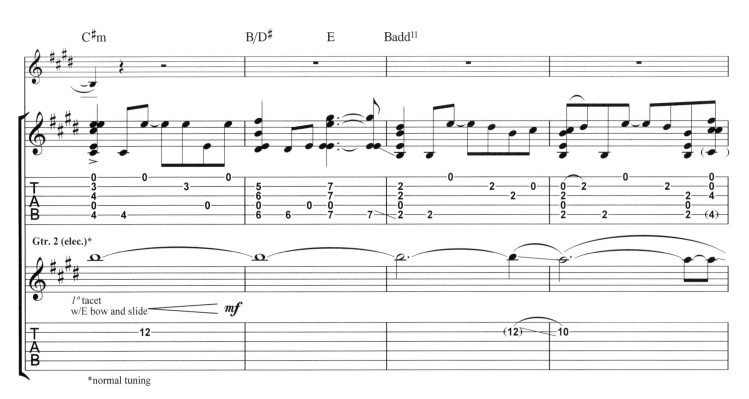

183

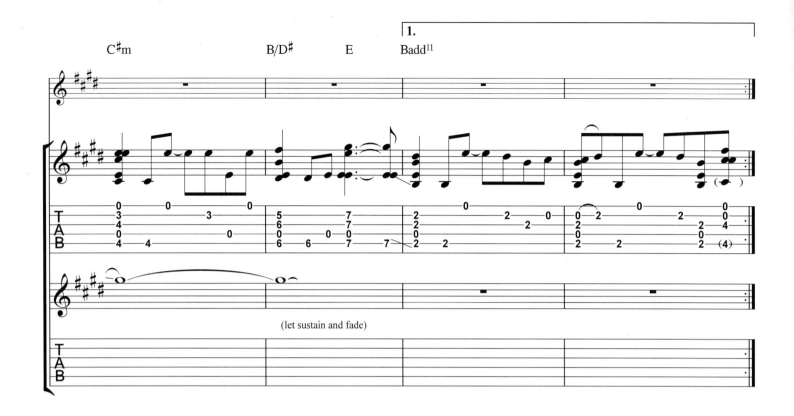

(let sustain and fade)

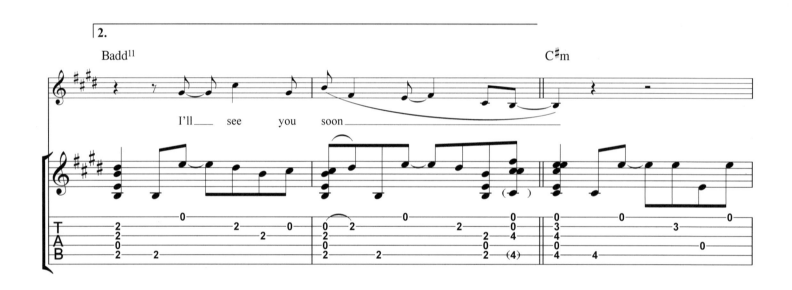

I'll___ see you soon_____

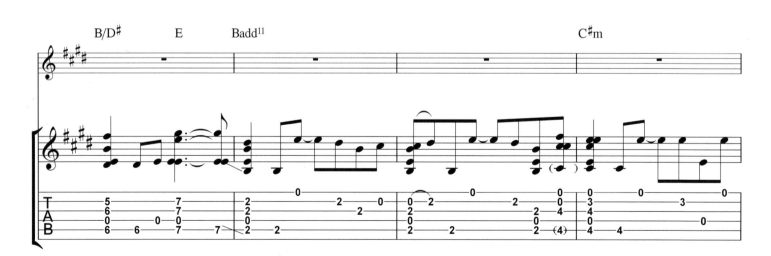

184

SLEEPING SUN

Words & Music by
Guy Berryman, Jon Buckland, Will Champion & Chris Martin

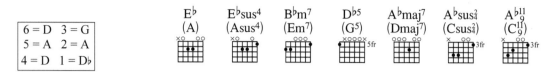

Capo 6th fret

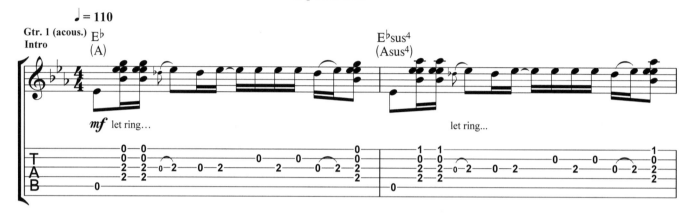

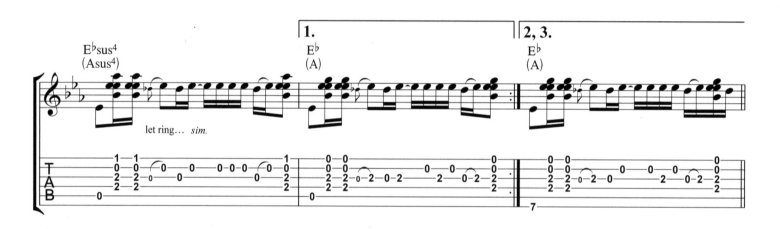

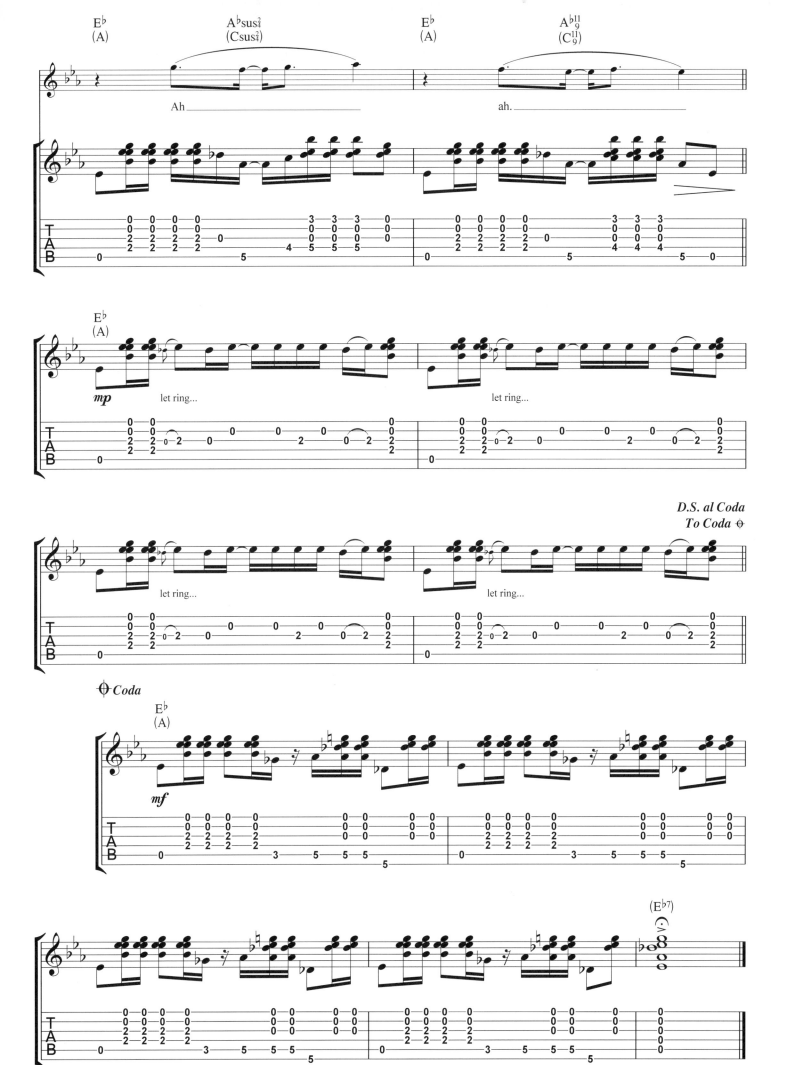

SPEED OF SOUND

Words & Music by
Guy Berryman, Jon Buckland, Will Champion & Chris Martin

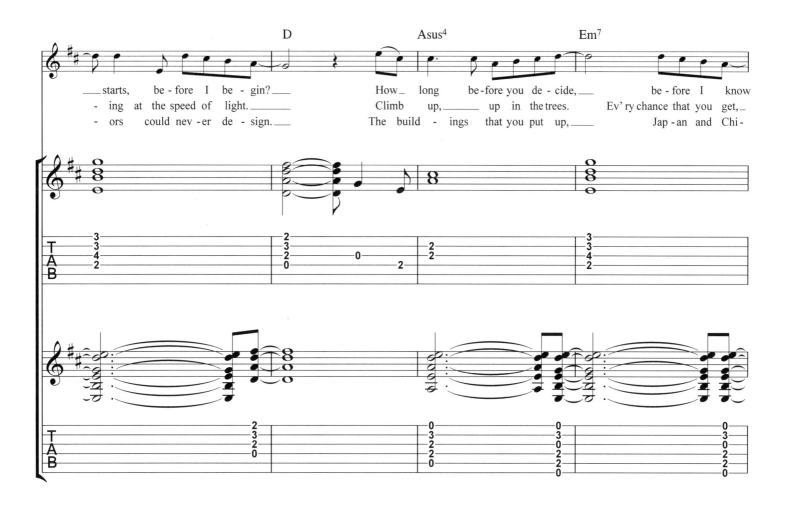

starts, be - fore I be - gin?___ How___ long be - fore you de - cide,___ be - fore I know
- ing at the speed of light.___ Climb up,___ up in the trees. Ev'ry chance that you get,___
- ors could nev - er de - sign.___ The build - ings that you put up,___ Jap - an and Chi -

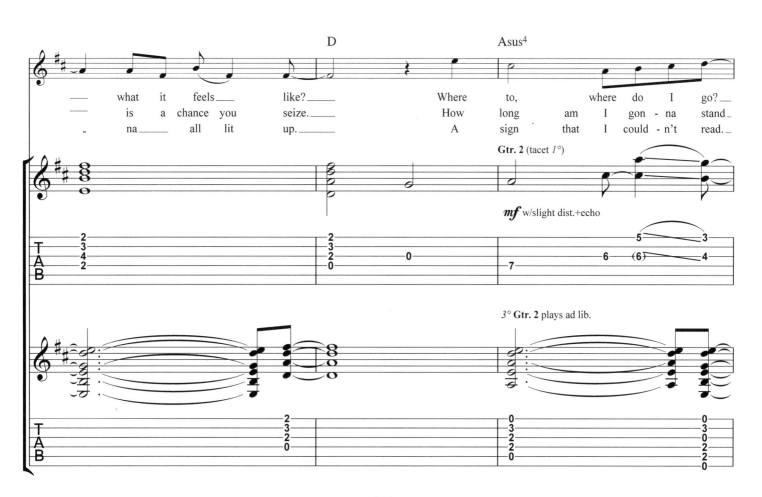

___ what it feels___ like?___ Where to, where do I go?___
___ is a chance you seize.___ How long am I gon - na stand___
- na all lit up.___ A sign that I could - n't read.___

If you nev - er try___ then you'll nev - er know.___ How___
with my head stuck un - der sand?___ I'll
Or a light that I could - n't see.___ Some___

long do I have to climb,___ up on the side___ of this moun tain of mine?___
start be - fore I can stop,___ be - fore I see___ things the right way___ up.___
things you have to be - lieve,___ oth - ers are puz - zles,___ puz - zl - ing me.___

1.

Interlude
Gtr. 1

let ring
Gtr. 2 tacet

2. Look

2, 3. **Pre-chorus**

All that noise___ and all that sound.___

mf let ring
w/slight dist.

Gtr. 3

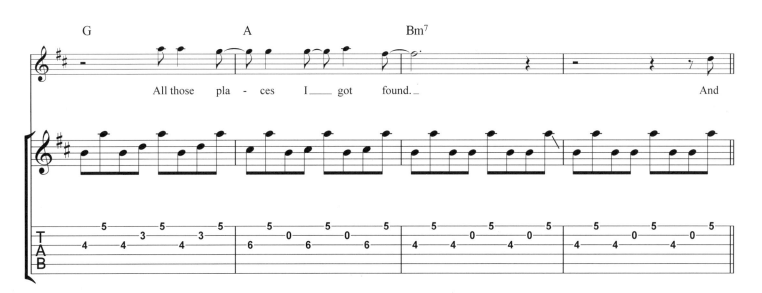

All those pla - ces I___ got found.___

And

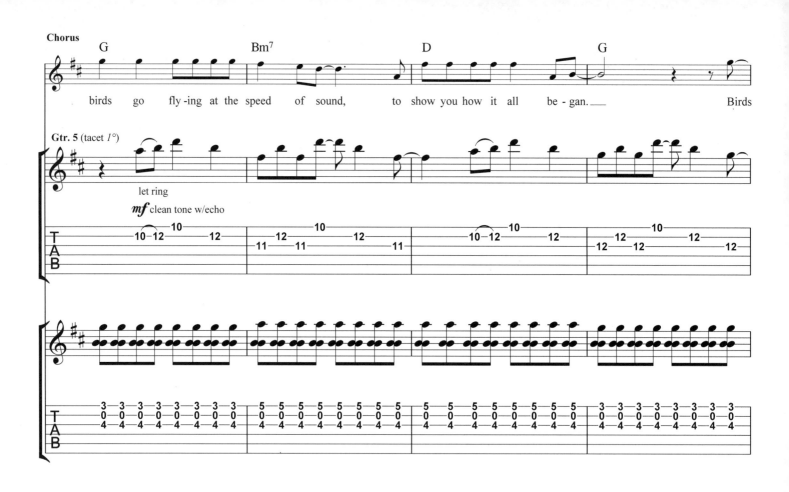

birds go fly-ing at the speed of sound, to show you how it all be-gan.___ Birds

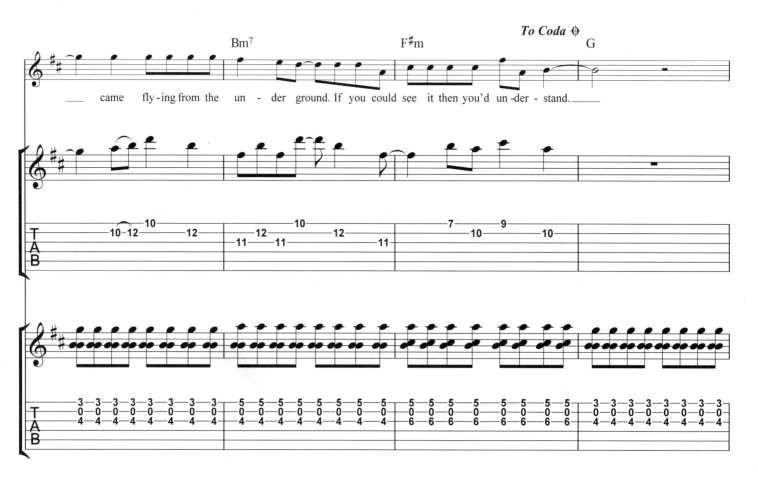

___ came fly-ing from the un - der ground. If you could see it then you'd un -der - stand.___

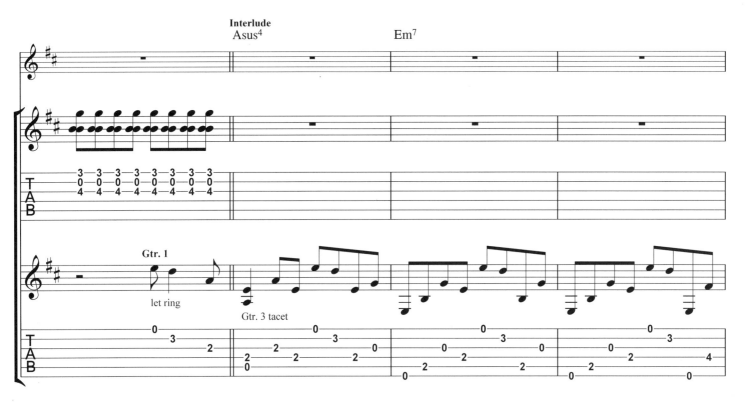

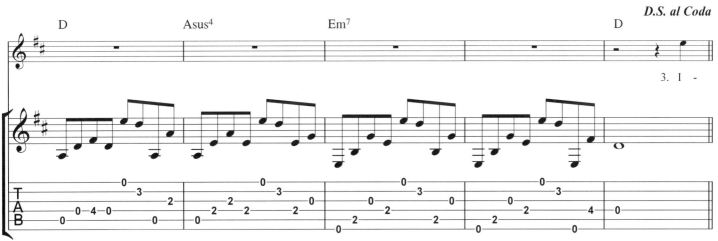

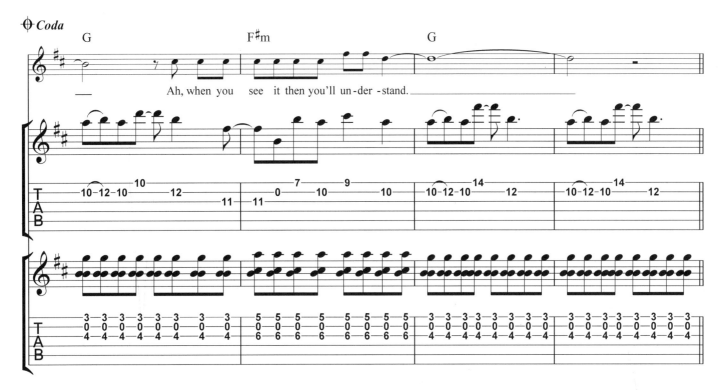

195

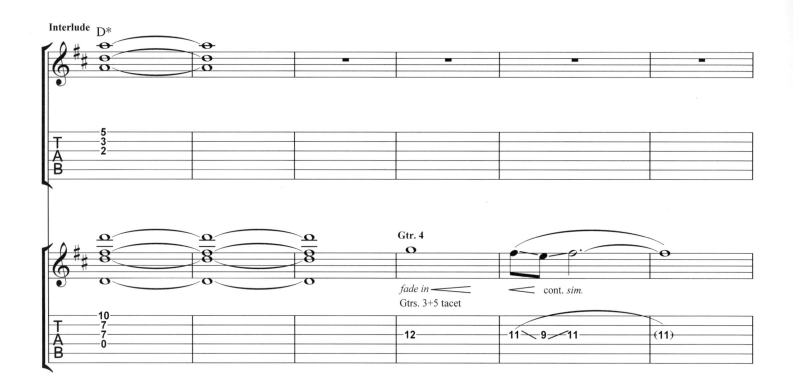

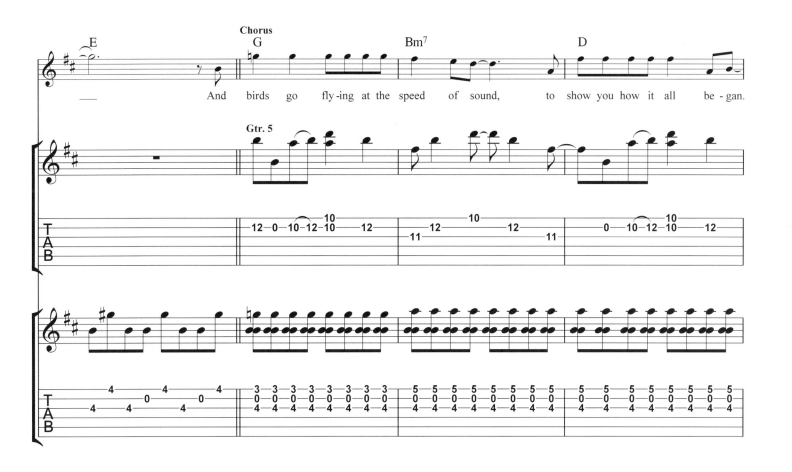

And birds go fly-ing at the speed of sound, to show you how it all be-gan.

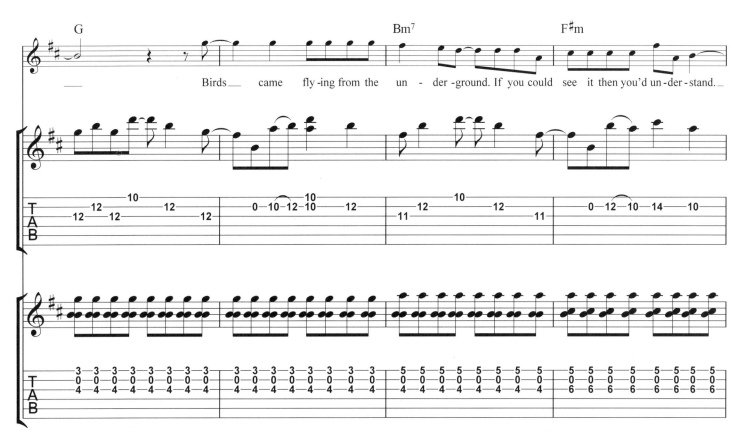

Birds__ came fly-ing from the un-der-ground. If you could see it then you'd un-der-stand.__

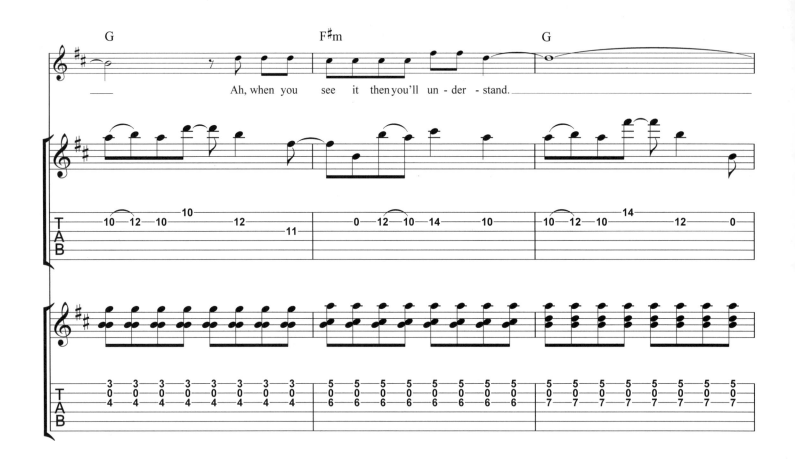

Ah, when you see it then you'll un - der - stand.

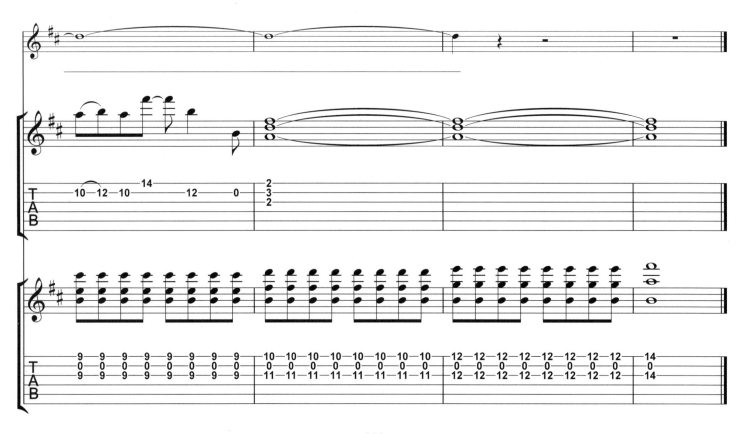

WHAT IF

Words & Music by
Guy Berryman, Jon Buckland, Will Champion & Chris Martin

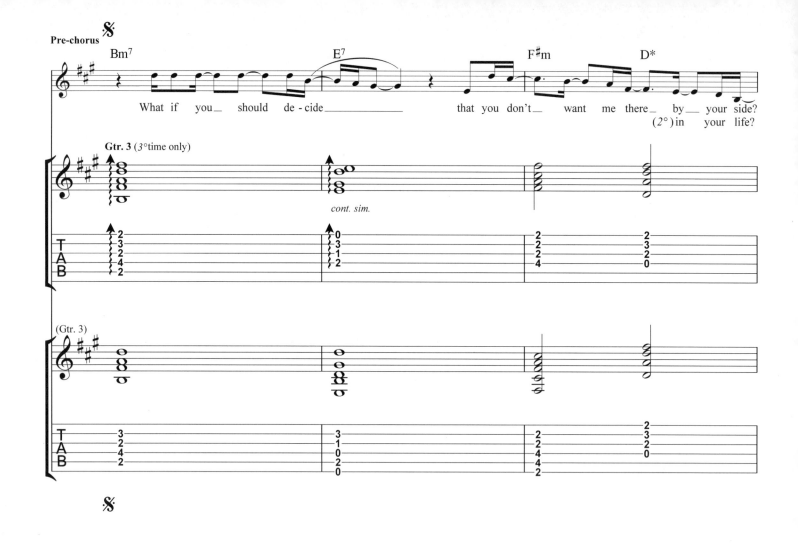

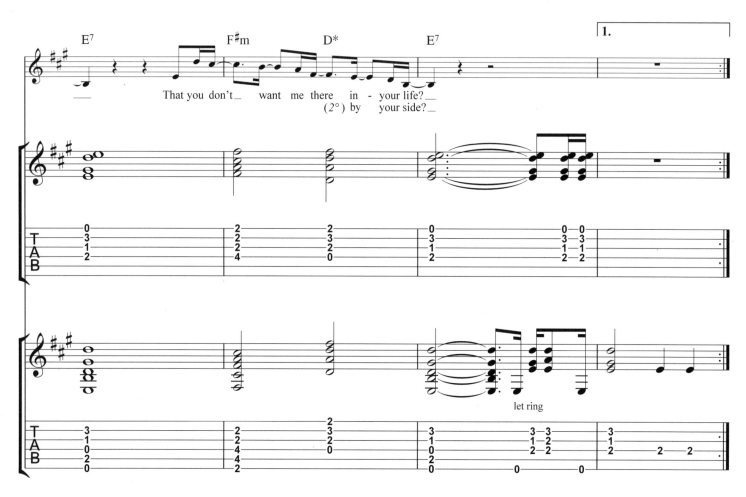

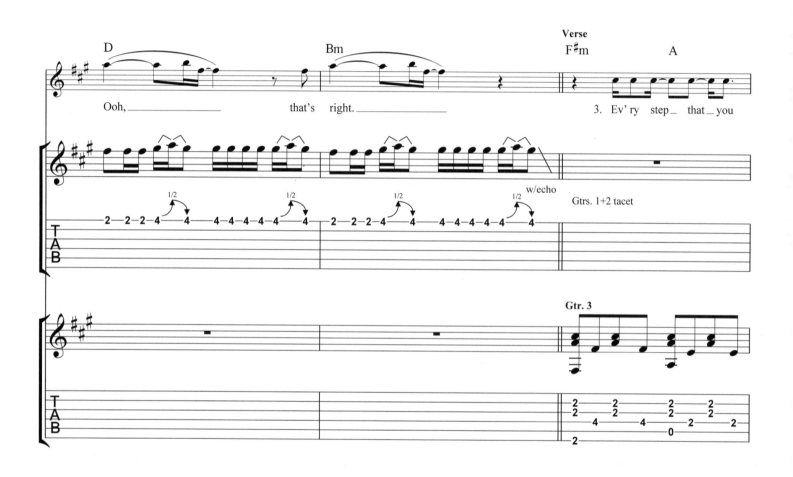

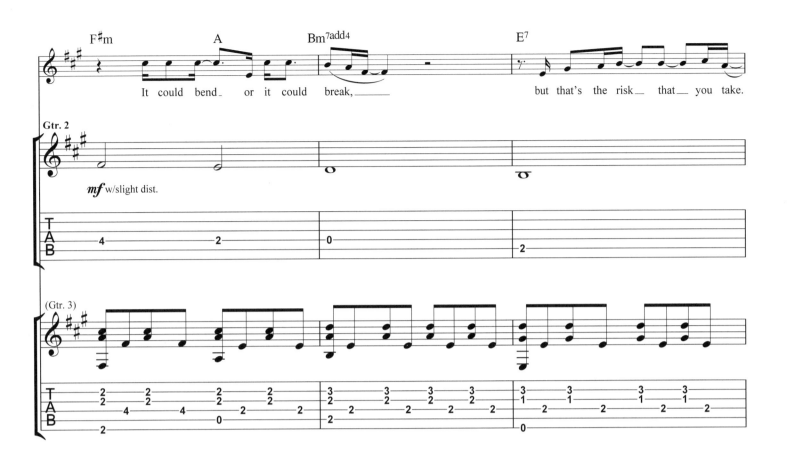

It could bend _ or it could break, _____ but that's the risk _ that _ you take.

Ooh, _____ that's right. _____

203

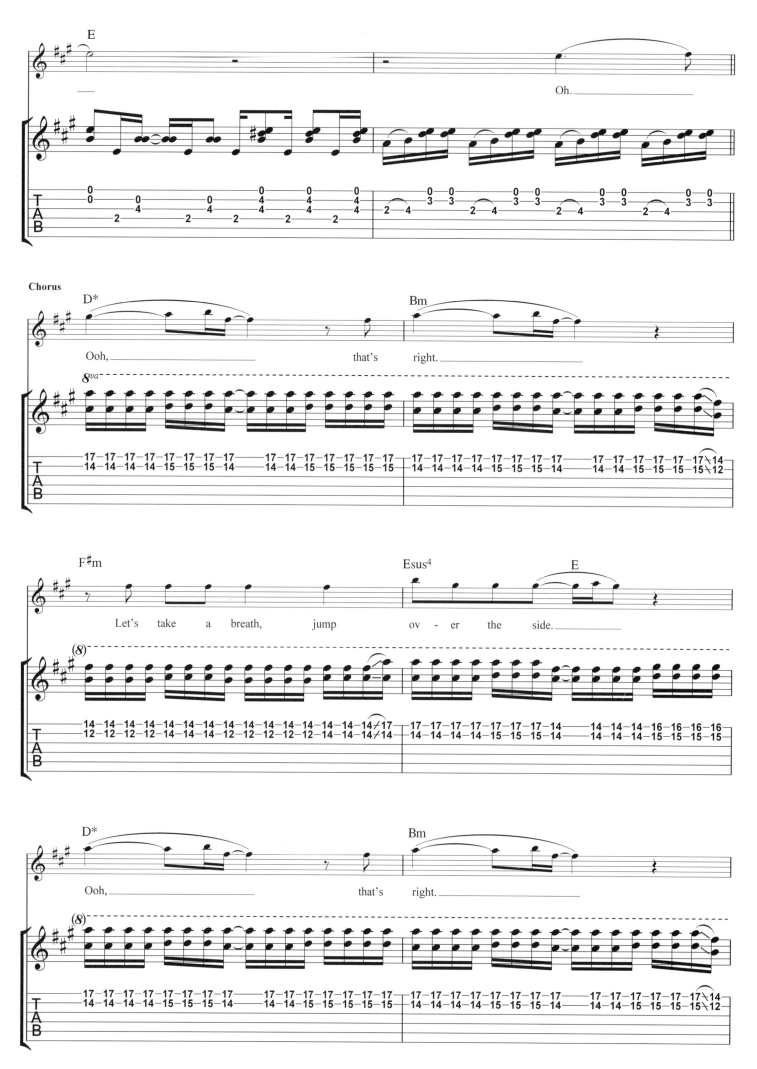

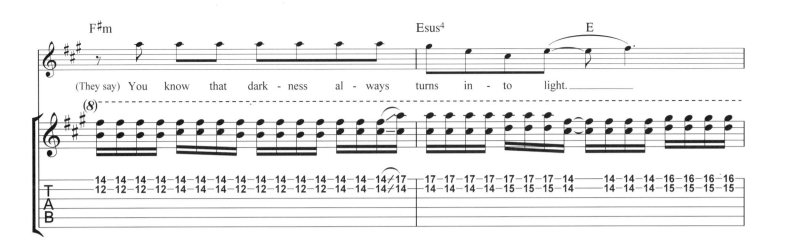

(They say) You know that dark - ness al - ways turns in - to light.____

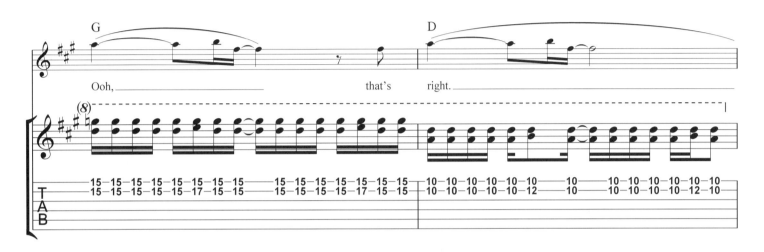

Ooh,____ that's right.____

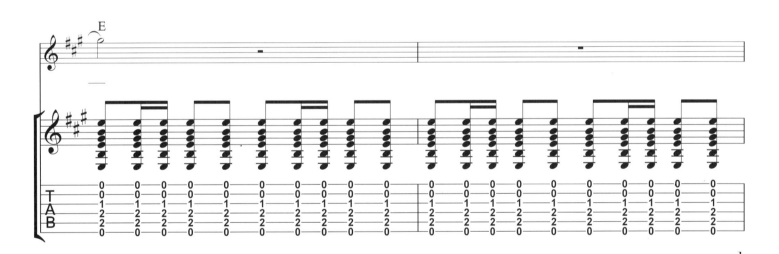

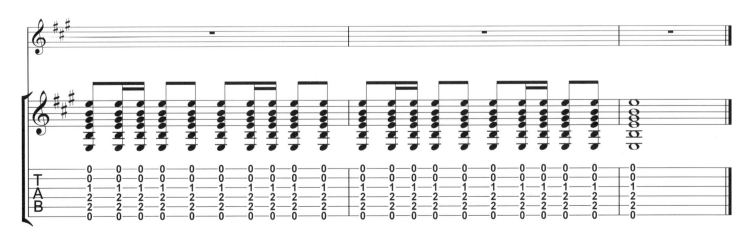

SUCH A RUSH

Words & Music by
Guy Berryman, Jon Buckland, Will Champion & Chris Martin

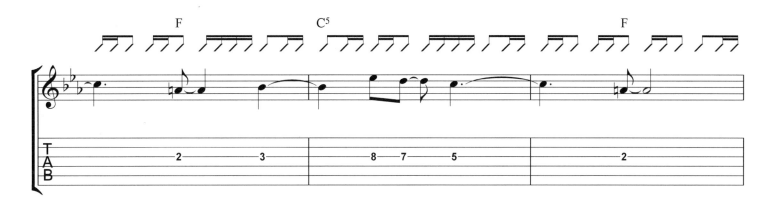

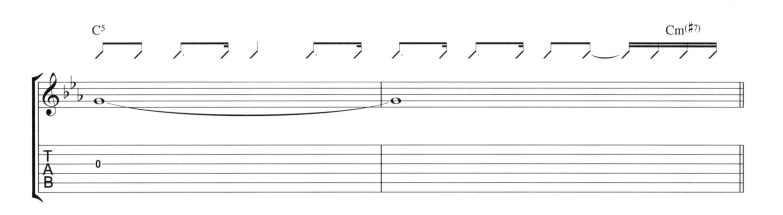

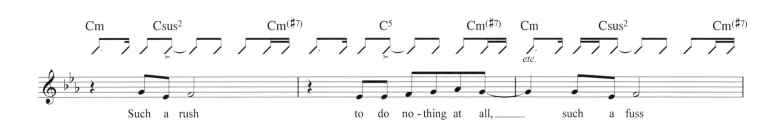

Such a rush to do no-thing at all,____ such a fuss to do no-thing at all,____ such a rush____ to do no-thing at____

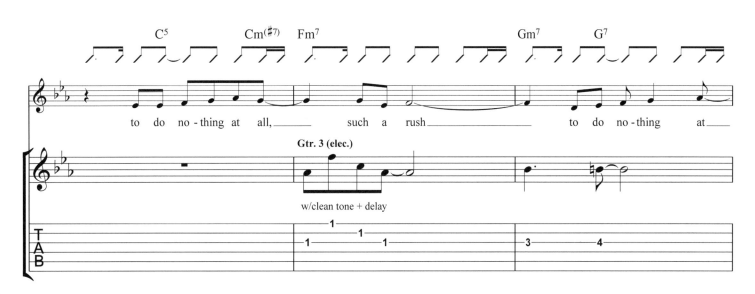

Gtr. 3 (elec.)

w/clean tone + delay

Interlude

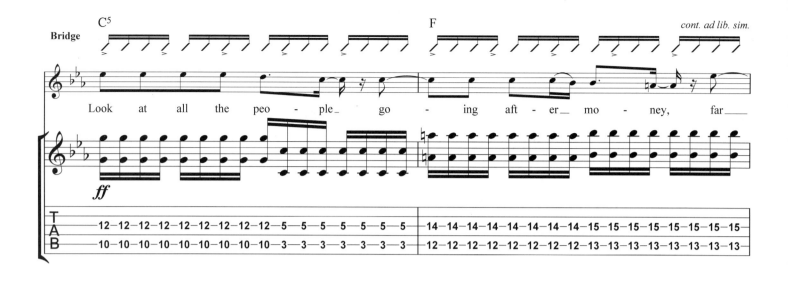

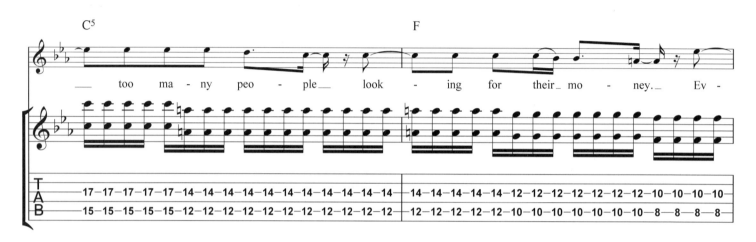

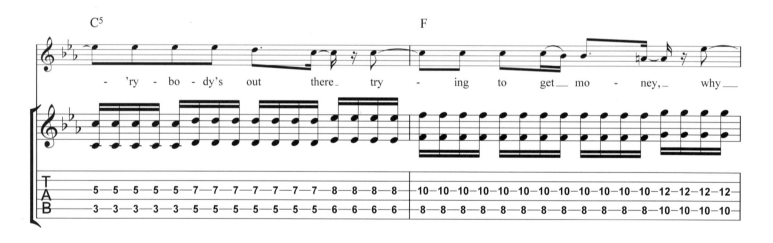

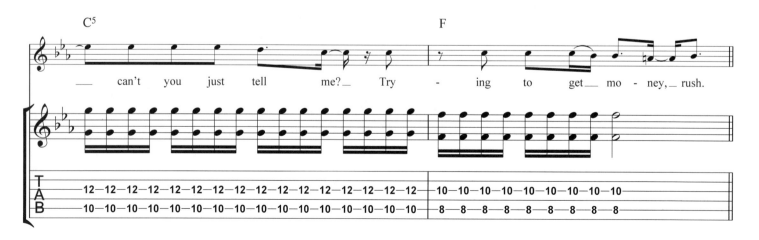

TALK

Words & Music by
Guy Berryman, Chris Martin, Karl Bartos, Jon Buckland,
Will Champion, Emil Schult & Ralf Hütter

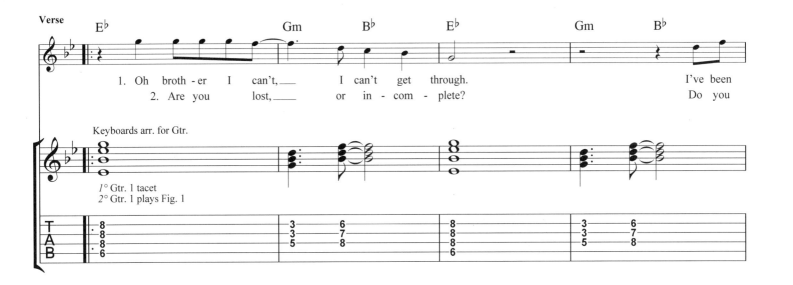

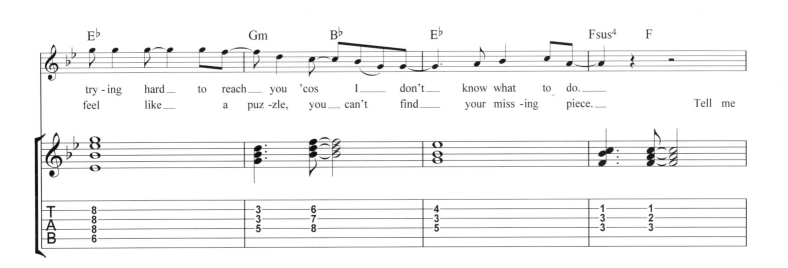

scared a-bout the fu - ture and I ___ want ___ to talk to you. ___ Oh, I want

feel like ___ they're talk - ing in a lan - guage I ___ don't speak. ___ And they're talk-

___ to talk to you. ___

- ing it ___ to me. ___ You could

Pre-chorus

take a pic-ture of some-thing you see. ___ In the fu-ture,

THINGS I DON'T UNDERSTAND

Words & Music by
Guy Berryman, Jon Buckland, Will Champion & Chris Martin

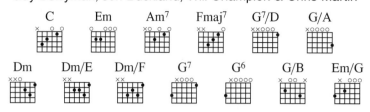

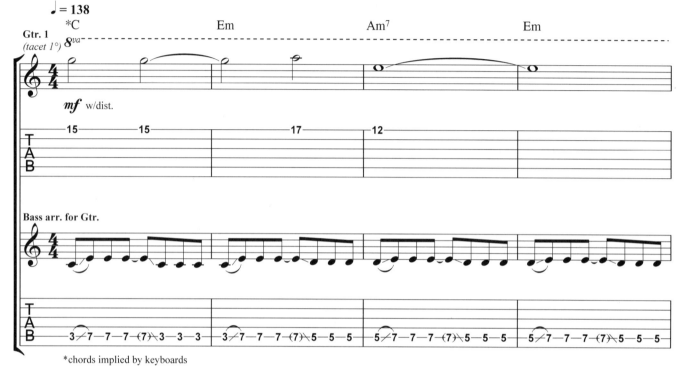

*chords implied by keyboards

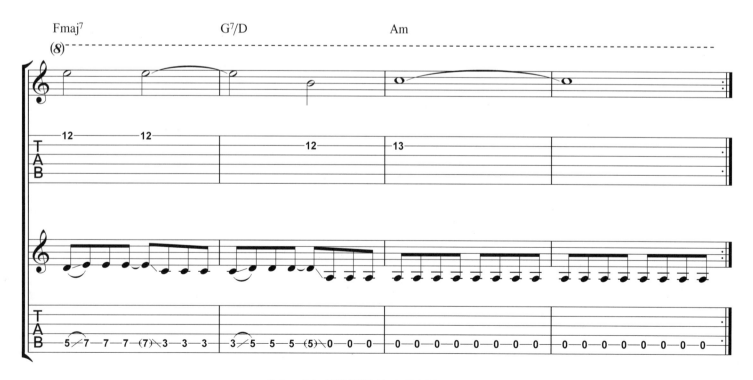

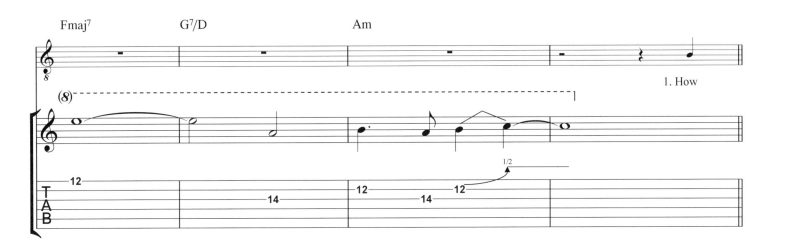

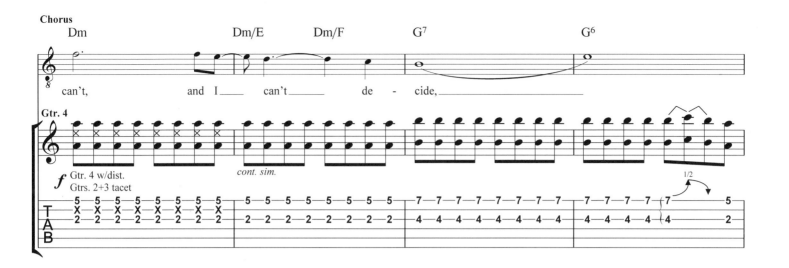

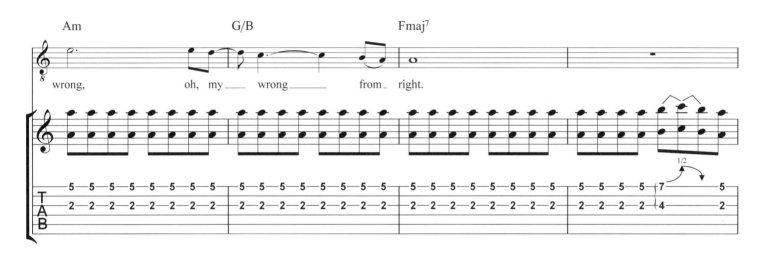

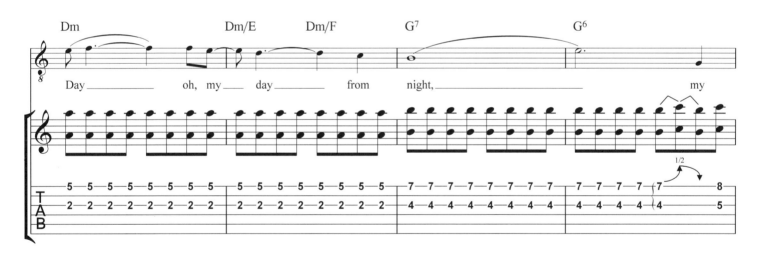

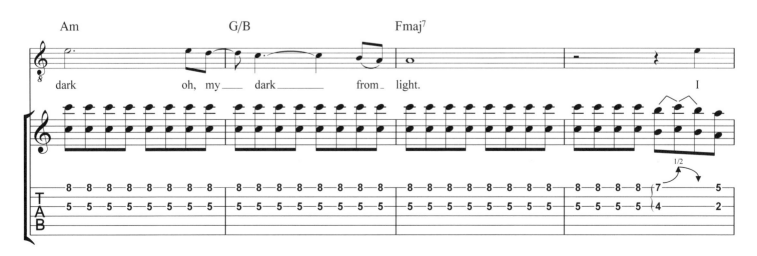

223

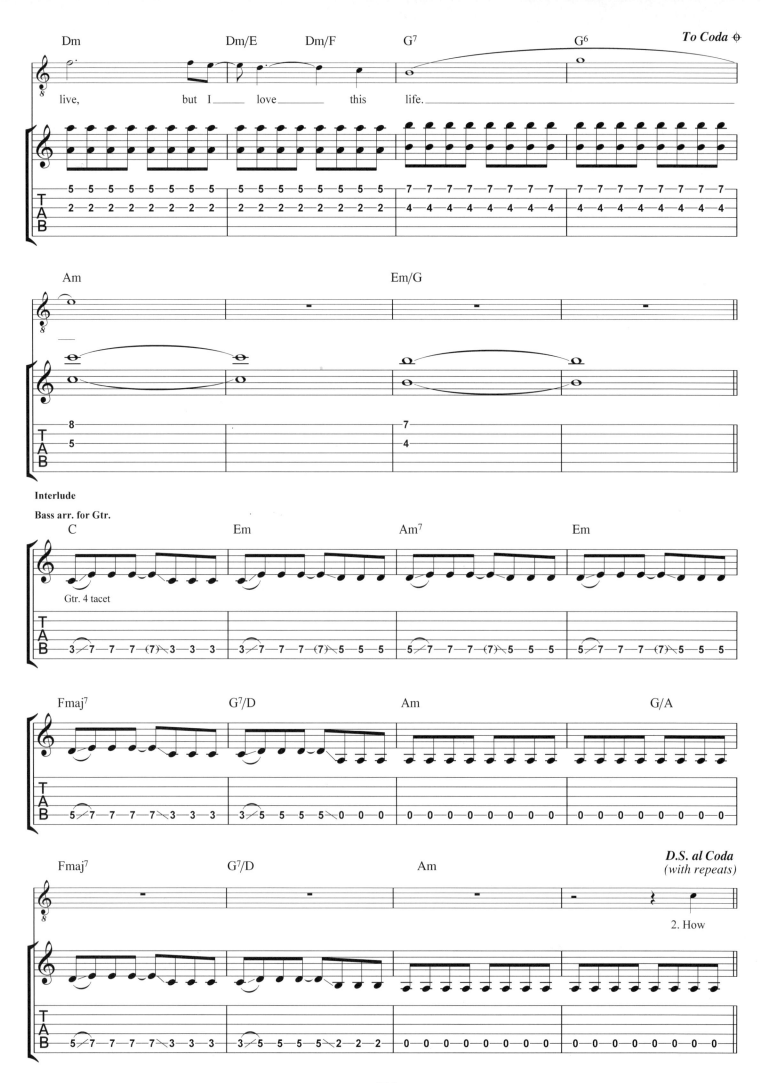

TROUBLE

Words & Music by
Guy Berryman, Jon Buckland, Will Champion & Chris Martin

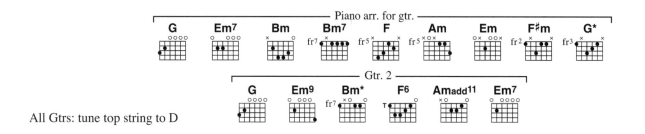

All Gtrs: tune top string to D

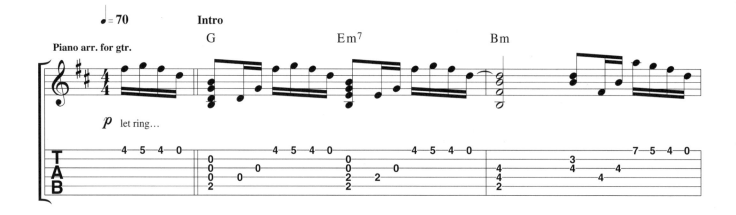

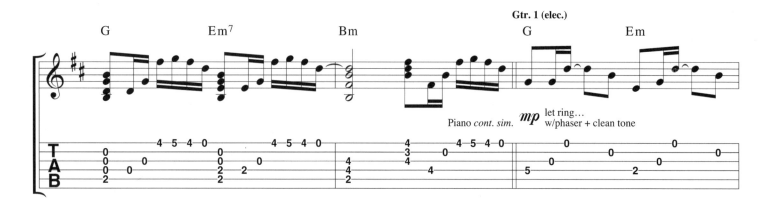

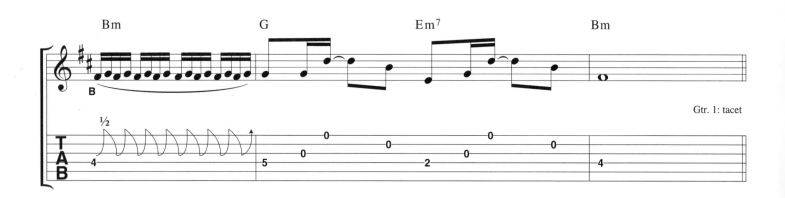

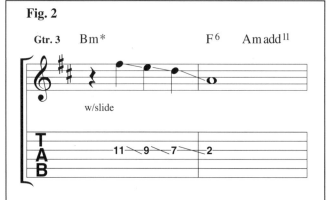

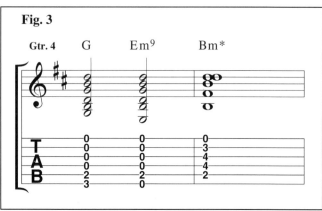

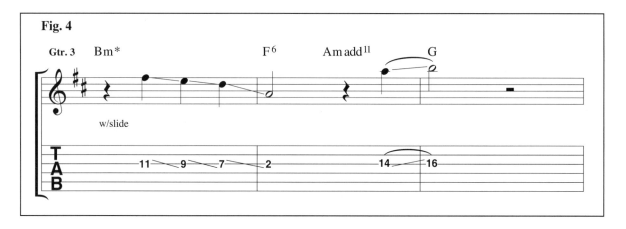

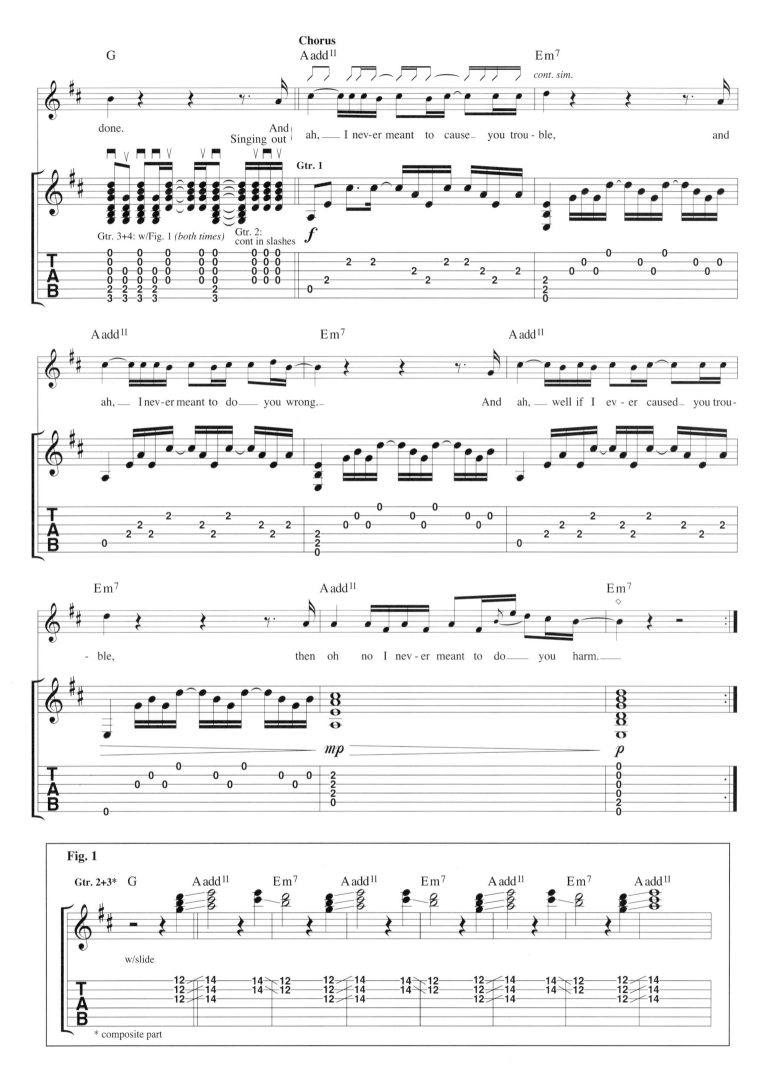

THE WORLD TURNED UPSIDE DOWN

Words & Music by
Guy Berryman, Jon Buckland, Will Champion & Chris Martin

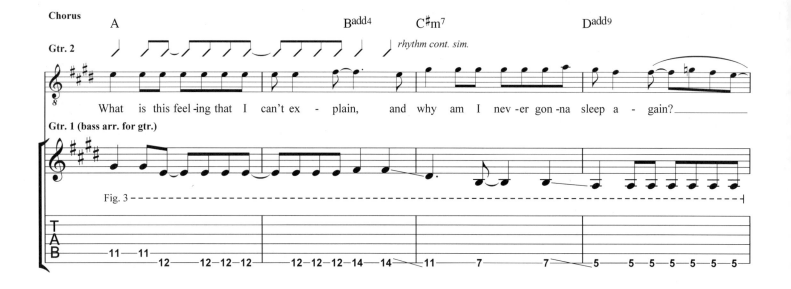

Chorus

Gtr. 2

A   B^{add4} C$^{\sharp}$m^7 D^{add9}

rhythm cont. sim.

What is this feel-ing that I can't ex - plain, and why am I nev-er gon-na sleep a - gain?____

Gtr. 1 (bass arr. for gtr.)

Fig. 3

Gtr. 1 plays Fig. 3

A   B^{add4} C$^{\sharp}$m^7 D^{add9}

____ What is this thing I've nev - er seen be - fore?____ A lit - tle boy, lost in a break - ing storm.____

A   B^{add4} C$^{\sharp}$m^7 D^{add9}

Hide and sob and a - way they fly.____ So write your name in the sum - mer sky.____

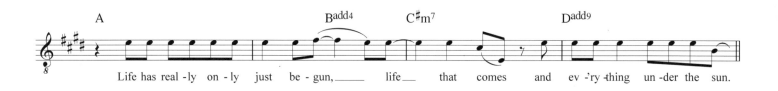

A   B^{add4} C$^{\sharp}$m^7 D^{add9}

Life has real -ly on - ly just be - gun,____ life__ that comes and ev -'ry -thing un - der the sun.

1.

Interlude E   E^7 E^6 E^7

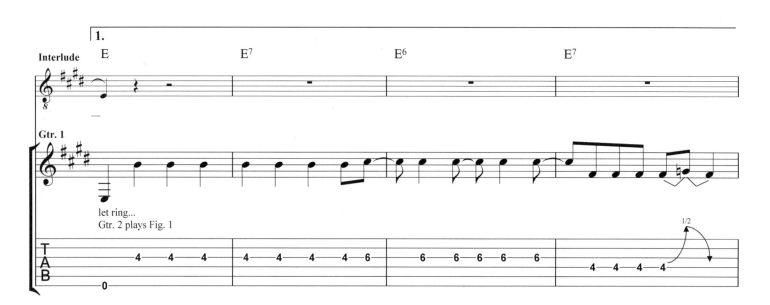

Gtr. 1

let ring...
Gtr. 2 plays Fig. 1

YELLOW

Words & Music by
Guy Berryman, Jon Buckland, Will Champion & Chris Martin

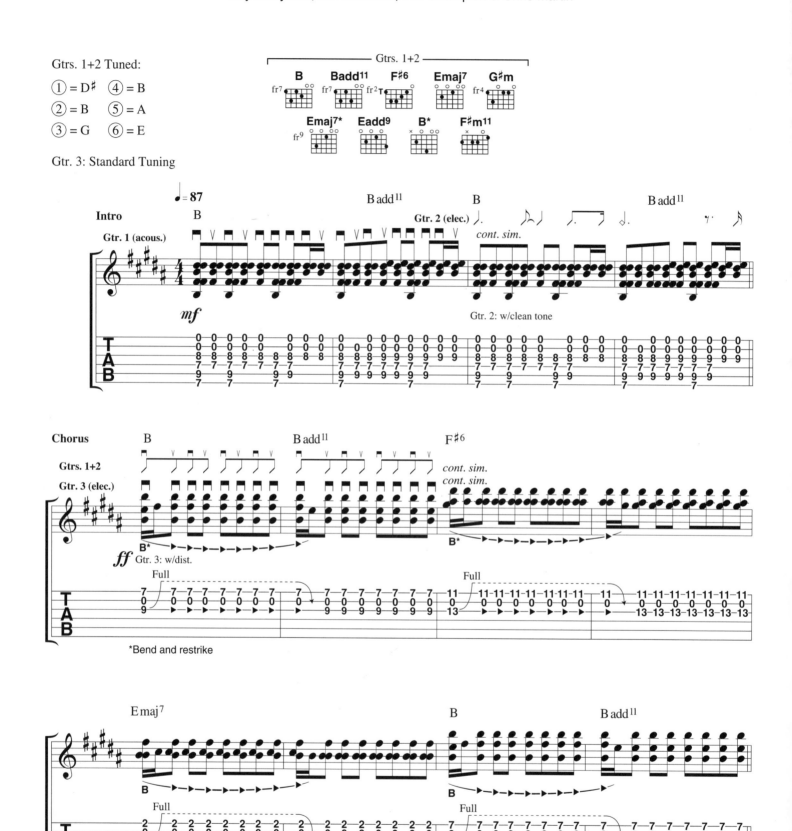

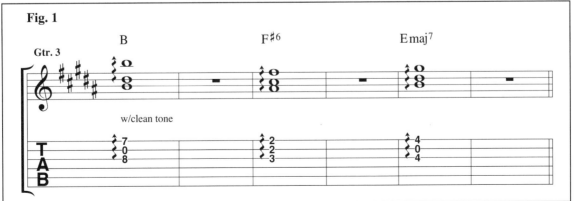

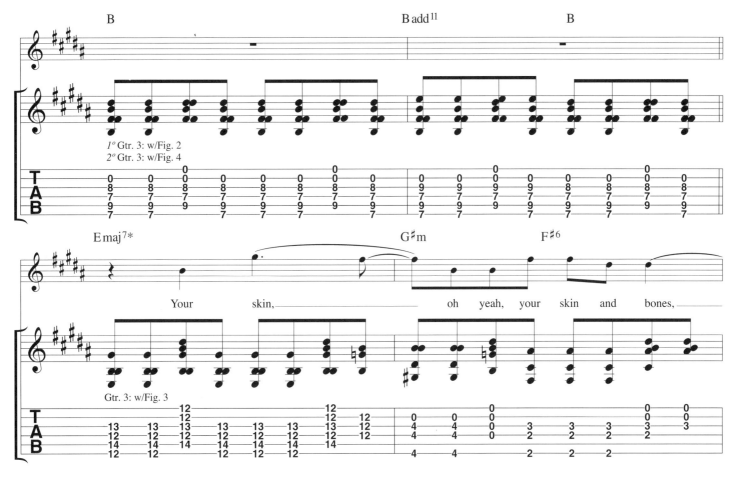

Your skin, _____ oh yeah, your skin and bones,

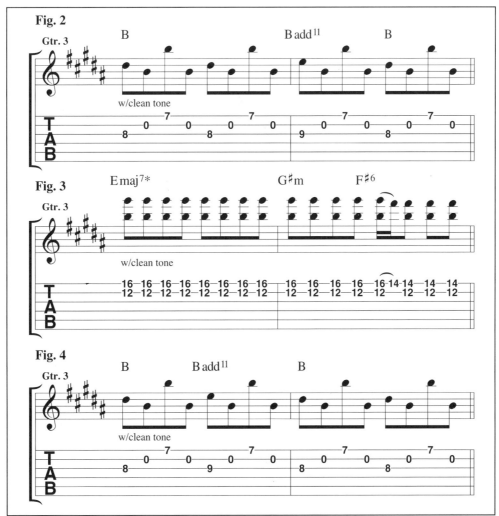

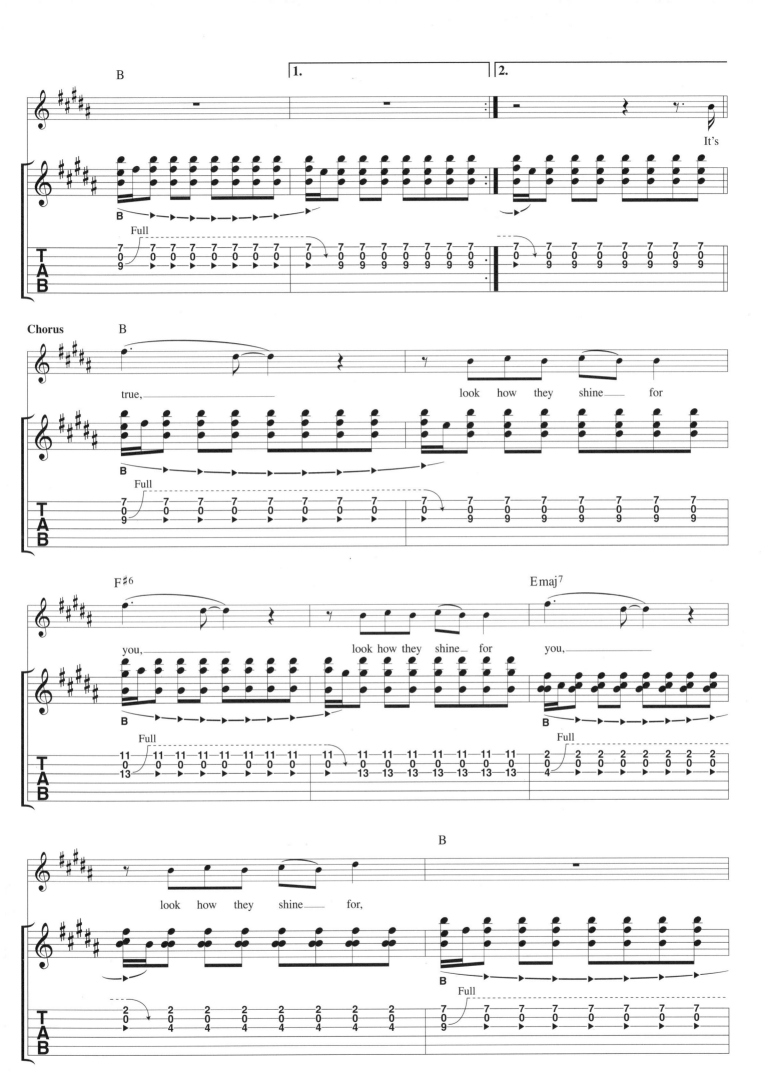